THE GIDEON SONGBOOK

THE GIDEONS INTERNATIONAL

P.O. BOX 140800 ● NASHVILLE, TENNESSEE 37214 ● U.S.A.

7-03
FORM 308

1 Send the Light

1. There's a call comes ring-ing o'er the rest-less wave: "Send the light!
2. We have heard the Mac-e-do-nian call to-day:
3. Let us pray that grace may ev-'ry-where a-bound:
4. Let us not grow wea-ry in the work of love.

"Send the light!

Send the light!" There are souls to res-cue, there are
And a gold - en of - f'ring at the
And a Christ - like spir - it ev - 'ry -
Send the light!" Let us gath - er jew - els for a

souls to save. Send the light! Send the light!
cross we lay.
where be found.
crown a - bove.
Send the light! Send the light!

Refrain

Send the light,_____ the bless-ed gos - pel light. Let it
Send the light,_____ and let its ra - diant beams Light the
Send the light, the bless - ed gos - pel light.
Send the light, and let its ra - diant beams

shine_____ from shore to shore.
world for-ev - er -
Let it shine
Light the world
from shore to shore!
more.
for - ev - er-more.

WORDS and MUSIC: Charles H. Gabriel, 1890

I Love to Tell the Story

A. Catherine Hankey

William G. Fischer

1. I love to tell the story Of un-seen things a-bove, Of Je-sus and His glo-ry, Of Je-sus and His love; I love to tell the story Be-cause I know 'tis true, It sat-is-fies my long-ings As noth-ing else can do.

2. I love to tell the story— More won-der-ful it seems Than all the gold-en fan-cies Of all our gold-en dreams; I love to tell the story— It did so much for me, And that is just the rea-son I tell it now to thee.

3. I love to tell the story— 'Tis pleas-ant to re-peat What seems,each time I tell it, More won-der-ful-ly sweet; I love to tell the story For some have nev-er heard The mes-sage of sal-va-tion From God's own ho-ly Word.

4. I love to tell the story, For those who know it best Seem hun-ger-ing and thirst-ing To hear it like the rest; And when in scenes of glo-ry I sing the new, new song, 'Twill be the old, old sto-ry That I have loved so long.

REFRAIN

I love to tell the sto-ry! 'Twill be my theme in glo-ry— To tell the old,old sto-ry Of Je-sus and His love.

3 We've a Story to Tell

H. Ernest Nichol

H. Ernest Nichol

1. We've a sto - ry to tell to the na - tions That shall turn their
2. We've a song to be sung to the na - tions That shall lift their
3. We've a mes - sage to give to the na - tions—That the Lord who
4. We've a Sav - ior to show to the na - tions Who the path of

hearts to the right, A sto - ry of truth and mer - cy, A
hearts to the Lord, A song that shall con - quer e - vil And
reign- eth a - bove Hath sent us His Son to save us And
sor - row hath trod, That all of the world's great peo - ples Might

sto - ry of peace and light, A sto - ry of peace and light.
shat - ter the spear and sword, And shat - ter the spear and sword.
show us that God is love, And show us that God is love.
come to the truth of God, Might come to the truth of God.

CHORUS

For the dark-ness shall turn to dawn-ing, And the dawn-ing to noon-day bright,

And Christ's great king-dom shall come to earth,, The king-dom of love and light.

Go Tell the Untold Millions

4

JOHN W. PETERSON

JOHN W. PETERSON

1. Out in the dark-ness of sin they are wait-ing,
2. Go in the pow-er the Lord will pro-vide you,
3. Moved and con-strained by the love of the Sav-ior,

Lost and a-way from the fold; Who'll bear the mes-sage of
Led by the Spir-it each day; You can-not fail on the
Leave friends and com-forts be-hind; Yield all your tal-ents and

Christ and re-demp-tion? See! they have nev-er been told. (been told.)
mis-sion He sends you— Go then, no long-er de-lay. (de-lay.)
time to His serv-ice— Go now, the lost ones to find. (to find.)

CHORUS

Go tell the un-told mil-lions O-ver the whole world wide;
far and wide;

Go tell the un-told mil-lions, Tell of the Cru-ci-fied.

5 Rescue the Perishing

FANNY J. CROSBY

WILLIAM H. DOANE

1. Res - cue the per-ish-ing, care for the dy - ing, Snatch them in
2. Tho they are slight-ing Him, still He is wait - ing, Wait - ing the
3. Down in the hu-man heart, crushed by the tempt - er, Feel - ings lie
4. Res - cue the per-ish-ing, du - ty de-mands it— Strength for thy

pit - y from sin and the grave; Weep o'er the err-ing one, lift up the
pen - i - tent child to re-ceive; Plead with them ear-nest-ly, plead with them
bur - ied that grace can re-store; Touched by a lov-ing heart, wak-ened by
la - bor the Lord will pro-vide; Back to the nar-row way pa-tient-ly

REFRAIN

fall - en, Tell them of Je - sus, the might-y to save.
gen - tly, He will for-give if they on - ly be-lieve.
kind - ness, Chords that are bro - ken will vi - brate once more.
win them, Tell the poor wan-d'rer a Sav - ior has died.

Res - cue the

per-ish-ing, Care for the dy-ing; Je-sus is mer-ci-ful, Je-sus will save.

So Send I You

6

E. Margaret Clarkson

John W. Peterson

1. So send I you to la-bor un-re-ward-ed, To serve un-
2. So send I you to bind the bruised and bro-ken, O'er wan-d'ring
3. So send I you to lone-li-ness and long-ing, With heart a-
4. So send I you to leave your life's am-bi-tion, To die to
5. So send I you to hearts made hard by ha-tred, To eyes made

paid, un-loved, un-sought, un-known, To bear re-buke, to suf-fer
souls to work, to weep, to wake, To bear the bur-dens of a
hung-'ring for the loved and known, For-sak-ing home and kin-dred,
dear de-sire, self-will re-sign, To la-bor long and love where
blind be-cause they will not see, To spend—tho it be blood—to

1-4 D.C.

scorn and scoff-ing— So send I you to toil for Me a-lone.
world a-wea-ry— So send I you to suf-fer for My sake.
friend and dear one— So send I you to know My love a-lone.
men re-vile you— So send I you to lose your life in Mine.
spend and spare not— So send I you to taste of Cal-va-

5

ry. "As the Fa-ther hath sent Me, So send I you."

7

Bringing In the Sheaves

KNOWLES SHAW

GEORGE A. MINOR

1. Sow-ing in the morn-ing, sow-ing seeds of kind-ness, Sow-ing in the
2. Sow-ing in the sun-shine, sow-ing in the shad-ows, Fear-ing nei-ther
3. Go-ing forth with weep-ing, sow-ing for the Mas-ter, Tho the loss sus-

noon-tide and the dew-y eve, Wait-ing for the har-vest and the
clouds nor win-ter's chill-ing breeze; By and by the har-vest and the
tained our spir-it oft-en grieves; When our weep-ing's o-ver He will

time of reap-ing— We shall come re-joic-ing, bring-ing in the sheaves.
la-bor end-ed— We shall come re-joic-ing, bring-ing in the sheaves.
bid us wel-come— We shall come re-joic-ing, bring-ing in the sheaves.

CHORUS

Bring-ing in the sheaves, bring-ing in the sheaves, We shall come re-

1. joic-ing, bring-ing in the sheaves.
2. joic-ing, bring-ing in the sheaves.

Work, for the Night Is Coming

9 Praise Him! Praise Him!

FANNY J. CROSBY

CHESTER G. ALLEN

1. Praise Him! praise Him! Je-sus, our bless-ed Re-deem-er! Sing, O
2. Praise Him! praise Him! Je-sus, our bless-ed Re-deem-er! For our
3. Praise Him! praise Him! Je-sus, our bless-ed Re-deem-er! Heav'n-ly

earth— His won-der-ful love pro-claim! Hail Him! hail Him! high-est arch-
sins He suf-fered and bled and died; He our Rock, our hope of e-
por-tals loud with ho-san-nas ring! Je-sus, Sav-ior, reign-eth for

an-gels in glo-ry, Strength and hon-or give to His ho-ly name!
ter-nal sal-va-tion, Hail Him! hail Him! Je-sus the Cru-ci-fied.
ev-er and ev-er, Crown Him! crown Him! Proph-et and Priest and King!

Like a shep-herd Je-sus will guard His chil-dren— In His arms He
Sound His prais-es— Je-sus who bore our sor-rows— Love un-bound-ed,
Christ is com-ing, o-ver the world vic-to-rious— Pow'r and glo-ry

REFRAIN

car-ries them all day long: Praise Him! praise Him! tell of His
won-der-ful, deep and strong:
un-to the Lord be-long:

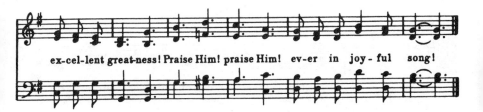

ex-cel-lent great-ness! Praise Him! praise Him! ev-er in joy-ful song!

Seek Ye First

10

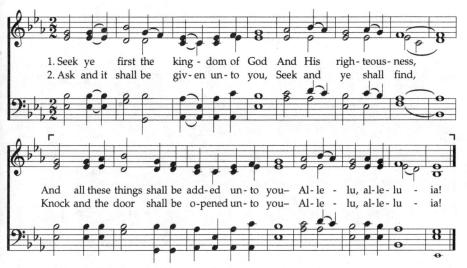

1. Seek ye first the king-dom of God And His righ-teous-ness,
2. Ask and it shall be giv-en un-to you, Seek and ye shall find,

And all these things shall be add-ed un-to you— Al-le-lu, al-le-lu - ia!
Knock and the door shall be o-pened un-to you— Al-le-lu, al-le-lu - ia!

COMPOSER: Karen Lafferty

11   To God Be the Glory

FANNY J. CROSBY   WILLIAM H. DOANE

1. To God be the glo-ry—great things He hath done! So loved He the
2. O per-fect re-demp-tion, the pur-chase of blood! To ev-'ry be-
3. Great things He hath taught us, great things He hath done, And great our re-

world that He gave us His Son, Who yield-ed His life an a-
liev-er the prom-ise of God; The vil-est of-fen-der who
joic-ing thru Je-sus the Son; But pur-er and high-er and

Fine

tone-ment for sin And o-pened the Life-gate that all may go in.
tru-ly be-lieves, That mo-ment from Je-sus a par-don re-ceives.
great-er will be Our won-der, our trans-port, when Je-sus we see.

D. S.—Je-sus the Son, And give Him the glo-ry—great things He hath done.

CHORUS

Praise the Lord, Praise the Lord, Let the earth hear His voice! Praise the Lord,

D. S.

Praise the Lord, Let the peo-ple re-joice! O come to the Fa-ther thru

Isn't the Love of Jesus Something Wonderful!   12

JOHN W. PETERSON   JOHN W. PETERSON

1. There will nev-er be a sweet-er sto - ry— Sto - ry of the Sav-ior's
2. Bound-less as the u - ni-verse a-round me, Reach-ing to the far-thest
3. Love be-yond our hu-man com-pre-hend- ing, Love of God in Christ—how

love di - vine,   Love that bro't Him from the realms of glo - ry
soul a - way—   Sav-ing, keep-ing love it was that found me,
can it be!   This will be my theme and nev- er end - ing,

Just to save a sin-ful soul like mine.
That is why my heart can tru - ly say:
Great re-deem-ing love of Cal-va - ry.

CHORUS

Is-n't the love of Je-sus some-thing won-der-ful, won-der-ful, won-der-ful; O is-n't the love of
     it is

Je-sus some-thing won-der-ful! Won-der-ful it is to me.
     to me.

13 Wonderful, Wonderful Jesus!

ANNA B. RUSSELL

ERNEST O. SELLERS

1. There is nev-er a day so drear-y, There is nev-er a night so
2. There is nev-er a cross so heav-y, There is nev-er a weight of
3. There is nev-er a care or bur-den, There is nev-er a grief or
4. There is nev-er a guilt-y sin-ner, There is nev-er a wan-d'ring

long, But the soul that is trust-ing Je-sus Will some-where
woe, But that Je-sus will help to car-ry Be-cause He
loss, But that Je-sus in love will light-en When car-ried
one, But that God can in mer-cy par-don Thru Je-sus

Chorus

find a song.
lov-eth so.
to the cross.
Christ, His Son.

Won-der-ful, won-der-ful Je-sus! In the

heart He im-plant-eth a song; A song of de-liv-'rance,

im-plant-eth a song;

of cour-age, of strength— In the heart He im-plant-eth a song.

Leaning on the Everlasting Arms

Elisha A. Hoffman

Anthony J. Showalter

1. What a fel-low-ship, what a joy di-vine, Lean-ing on the ev-er-
2. O how sweet to walk in this pil-grim way, Lean-ing on the ev-er-
3. What have I to dread, what have I to fear, Lean-ing on the ev-er-

last - ing arms; What a bless-ed-ness, what a peace is mine,
last - ing arms; O how bright the path grows from day to day,
last - ing arms? I have bless-ed peace with my Lord so near,

Lean-ing on the ev-er-last-ing arms.

REFRAIN

Lean - ing, Lean-ing on Je - sus,
lean - ing, lean-ing on Je - sus, Safe and se-cure from all a-larms; Lean - Lean-ing on

ing, lean - ing, Lean-ing on the ev-er-last-ing arms.
Je - sus, lean-ing on Je - sus,

15

Springs of Living Water

JOHN W. PETERSON

JOHN W. PETERSON

1. I thirst-ed in the bar-ren land of sin and shame, And noth-ing sat-is-
2. How sweet the liv-ing wa-ter from the hills of God, It makes me glad and
3. O sin-ner, won't you come to-day to Cal-va-ry? A foun-tain there is

fy-ing there I found; But to the bless-ed cross of Christ one
hap-py all the way; Now glo-ry, grace and bless-ing mark the
flow-ing deep and wide; The Sav-ior now in-vites you to the

day I came, Where springs of liv-ing wa-ter did a-bound.
path I've trod, I'm shout-ing "Hal-le-lu-jah" ev-'ry day.
wa-ter free, Where thirst-ing spir-its can be sat-is-fied.

CHORUS

Drink-ing at the springs of liv-ing wa-ter, Hap-py now am
Hap-py

I, My soul they sat-is-fy; Drink-ing at the
now am I, My soul they sat-is-fy; I'm

springs of liv - ing wa - ter, O won - der - ful and boun - ti - ful sup - ply!

My Faith Looks Up to Thee 16

1. My faith looks up to Thee, Thou Lamb of Cal - va - ry,
2. May Thy rich grace im - part Strength to my faint - ing heart,
3. While life's dark maze I tread, And griefs a - round me spread,
4. When ends life's tran - sient dream, When death's cold, sul - len stream

Sav - ior di - vine! Now hear me while I pray; Take all my
My zeal in - spire. As Thou hast died for me, O may my
Be Thou my Guide. Bid dark - ness turn to day; Wipe sor - row's
Shall o'er me roll, Blest Sav - ior, then in love Fear and dis -

guilt a - way. O let me from this day Be whol - ly Thine!
love to Thee Pure, warm, and change - less be, A liv - ing fire!
tears a - way; Nor let me ev - er stray From Thee a - side!
trust re - move. O bear me safe a - bove— A ran - somed soul!

17 Since I Have Been Redeemed

Edwin O. Excell

Edwin O. Excell

1. I have a song I love to sing, Since I have been re-deemed,
2. I have a Christ that sat-is-fies, Since I have been re-deemed;
3. I have a wit-ness bright and clear, Since I have been re-deemed,
4. I have a home pre-pared for me, Since I have been re-deemed,

Of my Re-deem-er, Sav-ior, King— Since I have been re-deemed.
To do His will my high-est prize— Since I have been re-deemed.
Dis-pel-ling ev-'ry doubt and fear— Since I have been re-deemed.
Where I shall dwell e-ter-nal-ly— Since I have been re-deemed.

CHORUS

Since I have been re-deemed, Since I have been re-
Since I have been re-deemed, Since I have been re-deemed,

deemed, I will glo-ry in His name; Since I have been re-
Since I have been re-deemed, Since

deemed, I will glo-ry in my Sav-ior's name.
I have been re-deemed,

I've Found a Friend
18

James G. Small

George C. Stebbins

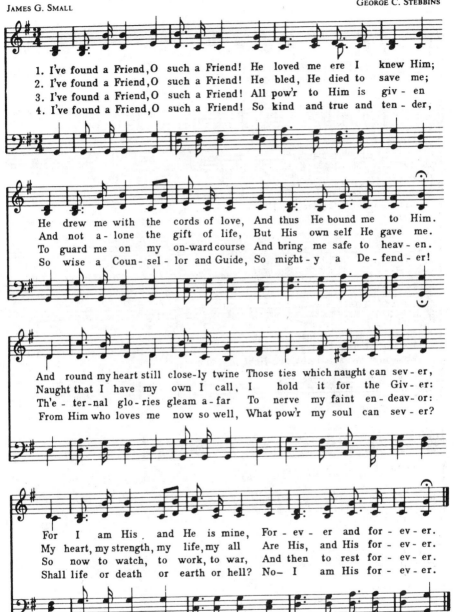

1. I've found a Friend, O such a Friend! He loved me ere I knew Him;
2. I've found a Friend, O such a Friend! He bled, He died to save me;
3. I've found a Friend, O such a Friend! All pow'r to Him is giv-en
4. I've found a Friend, O such a Friend! So kind and true and ten-der,

He drew me with the cords of love, And thus He bound me to Him.
And not a-lone the gift of life, But His own self He gave me.
To guard me on my on-ward course And bring me safe to heav-en.
So wise a Coun-sel-lor and Guide, So might-y a De-fend-er!

And round my heart still close-ly twine Those ties which naught can sev-er,
Naught that I have my own I call, I hold it for the Giv-er:
Th'e-ter-nal glo-ries gleam a-far To nerve my faint en-deav-or:
From Him who loves me now so well, What pow'r my soul can sev-er?

For I am His and He is mine, For-ev-er and for-ev-er.
My heart, my strength, my life, my all Are His, and His for-ev-er.
So now to watch, to work, to war, And then to rest for-ev-er.
Shall life or death or earth or hell? No— I am His for-ev-er.

19 Heavenly Sunlight

HENRY J. ZELLEY

GEORGE H. COOK

1. Walk-ing in sun-light all of my jour-ney, O-ver the moun-tains,
2. Shad-ows a-round me, shad-ows a-bove me, Nev-er con-ceal my
3. In the bright sun-light, ev-er re-joic-ing, Press-ing my way to

thru the deep vale: Je-sus has said, "I'll nev-er for-sake thee"—
Sav-ior and Guide; He is the Light, in Him is no dark-ness—
man-sions a-bove; Sing-ing His prais-es, glad-ly I'm walk-ing—

D.S. Hal-le-lu-jah! I am re-joic-ing,

Fine CHORUS

Prom-ise di-vine that nev-er can fail.
Ev-er I'm walk-ing close to His side. Heav-en-ly sun-light,
Walk-ing in sun-light, sun-light of love.

Sing-ing His prais-es— Je-sus is mine!

D.S.

heav-en-ly sun-light—Flood-ing my soul with glo-ry di-vine;

Redeemed

Fanny J. Crosby

William J. Kirkpatrick

1. Re-deemed—how I love to pro-claim it! Re-deemed by the
2. Re-deemed and so hap-py in Je-sus, No lan-guage my
3. I think of my bless-ed Re-deem-er, I think of Him
4. I know I shall see in His beau-ty The King in whose

blood of the Lamb; Re-deemed thru His in-fin-ite mer-cy—His
rap-ture can tell; I know that the light of His pres-ence With
all the day long; I sing, for I can-not be si-lent, His
law I de-light, Who lov-ing-ly guard-eth my foot-steps And

CHORUS

child, and for-ev-er, I am.
me doth con-tin-ual-ly dwell. Re - deemed, ____ re-
love is the theme of my song. re-deemed,
giv-eth me songs in the night.

deemed, ____ Re-deemed by the blood of the Lamb; Re-
re-deemed,

deemed, ____ re-deemed, ____ His child, and for-ev-er, I am.
re-deemed, re-deemed,

21 Heaven Came Down and Glory Filled My Soul

JOHN W. PETERSON

JOHN W. PETERSON

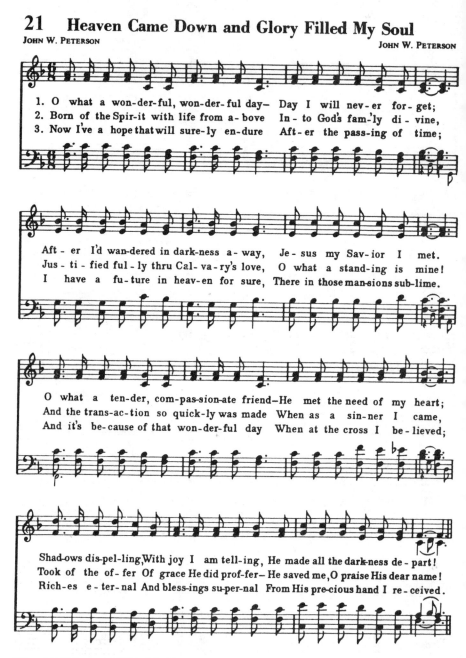

1. O what a won-der-ful, won-der-ful day— Day I will nev-er for-get;
2. Born of the Spir-it with life from a-bove In-to God's fam-'ly di-vine,
3. Now I've a hope that will sure-ly en-dure Aft-er the pass-ing of time;

Aft-er I'd wan-dered in dark-ness a-way, Je-sus my Sav-ior I met.
Jus-ti-fied ful-ly thru Cal-va-ry's love, O what a stand-ing is mine!
I have a fu-ture in heav-en for sure, There in those man-sions sub-lime.

O what a ten-der, com-pas-sion-ate friend—He met the need of my heart;
And the trans-ac-tion so quick-ly was made When as a sin-ner I came,
And it's be-cause of that won-der-ful day When at the cross I be-lieved;

Shad-ows dis-pel-ling, With joy I am tell-ing, He made all the dark-ness de-part!
Took of the of-fer Of grace He did prof-fer— He saved me, O praise His dear name!
Rich-es e-ter-nal And bless-ings su-per-nal From His pre-cious hand I re-ceived.

CHORUS

Heav-en came down and glo - ry filled my soul,
filled my soul, ___

When at the cross the Sav-ior made me whole;
made me whole; ___ My

sins were washed a - way ___ And my night was turned to day—

Heav-en came down and glo - ry filled my soul!
filled my soul! ___

CODA (*after last chorus only*)

Heav - en came down and glo - ry filled my soul! ___

22   It Is Glory Just to Walk with Him

AVIS B. CHRISTIANSEN   HALDOR LILLENAS

1. It is glo - ry just to walk with Him whose blood has ran-somed me,
2. It is glo - ry when the shad-ows fall to know that He is near,
3. 'Twill be glo - ry when I walk with Him on heav-en's gold-en shore,

It is rap-ture for my soul each day; It is joy di-vine to feel Him
O what joy to sim-ply trust and pray! It is glo - ry to a - bide in
Nev-er from His side a-gain to stray; 'Twill be glo - ry, won-drous glo - ry

near wher-e'er my path may be— Bless the Lord, it's glo - ry all the way!
Him when skies a-bove are clear—Yes, with Him it's glo - ry all the way!
with the Sav-ior ev - er-more—Ev - er - last-ing glo - ry all the way!

CHORUS

It is glo - ry just to walk with Him, It is glo - ry
with Him,

just to walk with Him; He will guide my steps a-right Thru the
with Him;

vale and o'er the height— It is glo-ry just to walk with Him.

with Him.

At Calvary

23

WILLIAM R. NEWELL

DANIEL B. TOWNER

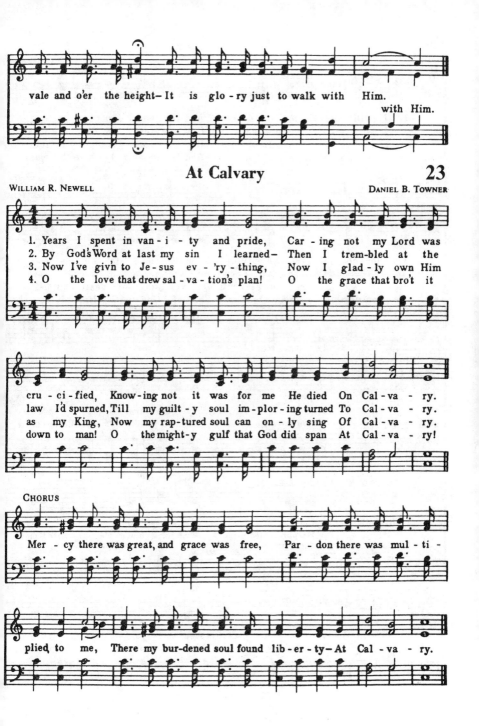

1. Years I spent in van - i - ty and pride, Car - ing not my Lord was
2. By God's Word at last my sin I learned— Then I trem-bled at the
3. Now I've giv'n to Je - sus ev - 'ry - thing, Now I glad - ly own Him
4. O the love that drew sal - va - tion's plan! O the grace that bro't it

cru - ci - fied, Know-ing not it was for me He died On Cal - va - ry.
law I'd spurned, Till my guilt - y soul im - plor - ing turned To Cal - va - ry.
as my King, Now my rap-tured soul can on - ly sing Of Cal - va - ry.
down to man! O the might - y gulf that God did span At Cal - va - ry!

CHORUS

Mer - cy there was great, and grace was free, Par - don there was mul - ti -

plied to me, There my bur-dened soul found lib - er - ty— At Cal - va - ry.

24 My Redeemer

PHILIP P. BLISS

JAMES McGRANAHAN

1. I will sing of my Re-deem-er And His won-drous love to me;
2. I will tell the won-drous sto-ry, How, my lost es-tate to save,
3. I will praise my dear Re-deem-er, His tri-um-phant pow'r I'll tell,
4. I will sing of my Re-deem-er And His heav'n-ly love to me;

On the cru-el cross He suf-fered, From the curse to set me free.
In His bound-less love and mer-cy, He the ran-som free-ly gave.
How the vic-to-ry He giv-eth O-ver sin and death and hell.
He from death to life hath bro't me, Son of God with Him to be.

CHORUS

Sing, O sing of my Re-deem-er,
of my Re-deem-er, Sing, O sing of my Re-deem-er,

With His blood He pur-chased me;
He pur-chased me, With His blood He pur-chased me;

On the cross He sealed my par-don,
He sealed my par-don, On the cross He sealed my par-don,

Paid the debt and made me free.

and made me free, and made me free.

Glory to His Name

25

ELISHA A. HOFFMAN

JOHN H. STOCKTON

1. Down at the cross where my Sav - ior died, Down where for cleans-ing from
2. I am so won-drous-ly saved from sin, Je - sus so sweet-ly a -
3. O pre-cious foun-tain that saves from sin, I am so glad I have
4. Come to this foun-tain so rich and sweet, Cast thy poor soul at the

sin I cried, There to my heart was the blood ap - plied—
bides with - in; There at the cross where He took me in—
en - tered in; There Je - sus saves me and keeps me clean—
Sav - ior's feet; Plunge in to - day, and be made com - plete—

REFRAIN

Glo-ry to His name. Glo-ry to His name, Glo-ry to His name;

There to my heart was the blood ap-plied— Glo-ry to His name.

26   My Savior's Love

CHARLES H. GABRIEL   CHARLES H. GABRIEL

1. I stand a-mazed in the pres-ence Of Je - sus the Naz-a - rene,
2. For me it was in the gar - den He prayed,"Not My will, but Thine;"
3. In pit - y an - gels be-held Him, And came from the world of light
4. He took my sins and my sor - rows, He made them His ver - y own;
5. When with the ran-somed in glo - ry His face I at last shall see,

And won-der how He could love me, A sin - ner condemned, un - clean.
He had no tears for His own griefs But sweat-drops of blood for mine.
To com-fort Him in the sor-rows He bore for my soul that night.
He bore the bur - den to Cal - v'ry And suf-fered and died a - lone.
'Twill be my joy thru the a - ges To sing of His love for me.

CHORUS

How mar-vel-ous! how won-der-ful! And my song shall ev - er be:
O how mar-vel-ous! O how won-der-ful!

How mar-vel-ous! how won-der-ful Is my Sav-ior's love for me!
O how mar-vel-ous! O how won-der-ful

When We All Get to Heaven

28 When the Roll Is Called Up Yonder

JAMES M. BLACK

JAMES M. BLACK

1. When the trum-pet of the Lord shall sound and time shall be no more, And the
2. On that bright and cloudless morning when the dead in Christ shall rise And the
3. Let us la-bor for the Mas-ter from the dawn till set-ting sun, Let us

morn-ing breaks e-ter-nal, bright and fair— When the saved of earth shall gath-er
glo-ry of His res-ur-rec-tion share— When His cho-sen ones shall gath-er
talk of all His won-drous love and care; Then when all of life is o-ver

o-ver on the oth-er shore, And the roll is called up yon-der—
to their home be-yond the skies, And the roll is called up yon-der—
and our work on earth is done, And the roll is called up yon-der—

CHORUS

I'll be there! When the roll is called up yon - der, When the
I'll be there!   When the roll is called up yon-der I'll be there,
I'll be there!

roll is called up yon - der, When the roll
When the roll is called up yon-der I'll be there,   When the roll

is called up yon - der—When the roll is called up yon-der I'll be there!

Revive Us Again

29

WILLIAM P. MACKAY.

JOHN J. HUSBAND

1. We praise Thee, O God, for the Son of Thy love, For Je - sus who
2. We praise Thee, O God, for Thy Spir- it of light, Who has shown us our
3. All glo - ry and praise to the Lamb that was slain, Who has borne all our
4. Re - vive us a - gain—fill each heart with Thy love; May each soul be re-

CHORUS

died and is   now gone a - bove.
Sav - ior and scat - tered our night.
sins and has cleansed ev - 'ry stain.   Hal-le - lu-jah, Thine the glo-ry! Hal-le-
kin - dled with fire from a - bove.

lu-jah, a - men! Hal-le - lu-jah, Thine the glo-ry! Re-vive us a - gain.

30 Sweet By and By

Sanford F. Bennett

Joseph P. Webster

1. There's a land that is fair-er than day, And by faith we can
2. We shall sing on that beau-ti-ful shore The me-lo-di-ous
3. To our boun-ti-ful Fa-ther a-bove We will of-fer our

see it a-far, For the Fa-ther waits o-ver the way To pre-
songs of the blest; And our spir-its shall sor-row no more— Not a
trib-ute of praise, For the glo-ri-ous gift of His love And the

CHORUS

pare us a dwell-ing-place there. In the sweet by and
sigh for the bless-ing of rest. In the sweet
bless-ings that hal-low our days.

by, We shall meet on that beau-ti-ful shore; In the
by and by, by and by,

sweet by and by, We shall meet on that beau-ti-ful shore.
In the sweet by and by,

O That Will Be Glory

CHARLES H. GABRIEL   CHARLES H. GABRIEL

1. When all my la-bors and tri-als are o'er And I am safe on that beau-ti-ful shore, Just to be near the dear Lord I a-dore Will thru the a-ges be glo-ry for me.

2. When, by the gift of His in-fi-nite grace, I am ac-cord-ed in heav-en a place, Just to be there and to look on His face Will thru the a-ges be glo-ry for me.

3. Friends will be there I have loved long a-go, Joy like a riv-er a-round me will flow; Yet, just a smile from my Sav-ior, I know, Will thru the a-ges be glo-ry for me.

CHORUS

O that will be glo-ry for me, Glo-ry for me, glo-ry for me; When by His grace I shall look on His face, That will be glo-ry, be glo-ry for me!

32 Saved by Grace

Fanny J. Crosby

George C. Stebbins
Arr. by Norman Johnson

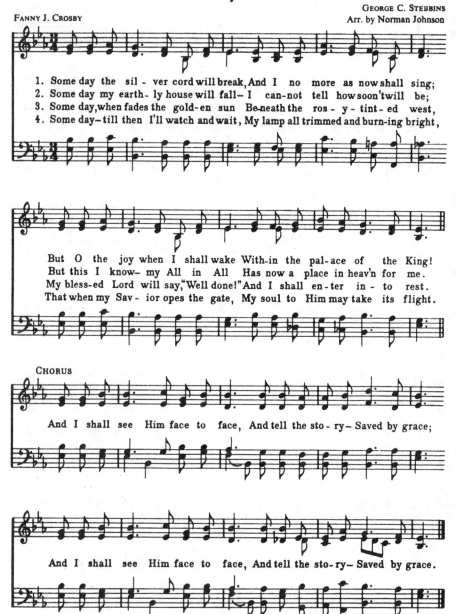

1. Some day the sil - ver cord will break, And I no more as now shall sing;
2. Some day my earth - ly house will fall— I can-not tell how soon 'twill be;
3. Some day, when fades the gold-en sun Be-neath the ros - y - tint - ed west,
4. Some day—till then I'll watch and wait, My lamp all trimmed and burn-ing bright,

But O the joy when I shall wake With-in the pal-ace of the King!
But this I know— my All in All Has now a place in heav'n for me.
My bless-ed Lord will say, "Well done!" And I shall en - ter in - to rest.
That when my Sav - ior opes the gate, My soul to Him may take its flight.

CHORUS

And I shall see Him face to face, And tell the sto - ry— Saved by grace;

And I shall see Him face to face, And tell the sto - ry— Saved by grace.

O God, Our Help in Ages Past

From Psalm 90
ISAAC WATTS
Attr. to William Croft

1. O God, our help in a-ges past, Our hope for years to come,
2. Un-der the shad-ow of Thy throne Still may we dwell se-cure;
3. Be-fore the hills in or-der stood Or earth re-ceived her frame,
4. Time, like an ev-er-roll-ing stream, Bears all its sons a-way;
5. O God, our help in a-ges past, Our hope for years to come,

Our shel-ter from the storm-y blast, And our e-ter-nal home!
Suf-fi-cient is Thine arm a-lone, And our de-fense is sure.
From ev-er-last-ing Thou art God, To end-less years the same.
They fly, for-got-ten, as a dream Dies at the ope-ning day.
Be Thou our guide while life shall last, And our e-ter-nal home.

What a Mighty God We Serve   34

What a might-y God we serve,   What a might-y God we
serve;   An-gels bow be-fore Him,   Heav-en and earth a-
dore Him,   What a might-y God we serve.

TEXT: Anonymous
MUSIC: Anonymous

35 Great Is Thy Faithfulness

Thomas O. Chisholm

William M. Runyan

1. Great is Thy faith-ful-ness, O God my Fa-ther! There is no
2. Sum-mer and win-ter, and spring-time and har-vest, Sun, moon and
3. Par-don for sin and a peace that en-dur-eth, Thine own dear

shad-ow of turn-ing with Thee; Thou chang-est not, Thy com-
stars in their cours-es a-bove, Join with all na-ture in
pres-ence to cheer and to guide, Strength for to-day and bright

pas-sions, they fail not: As Thou hast been Thou for-ev-er wilt be.
man-i-fold wit-ness To Thy great faith-ful-ness, mer-cy and love.
hope for to-mor-row— Bless-ings all mine, with ten thou-sand be-side!

CHORUS

Great is Thy faith-ful-ness! Great is Thy faith-ful-ness! Morn-ing by

morn-ing new mer-cies I see; All I have need-ed Thy

Words: Thomas O. Chisholm
Music: William M. Runyan

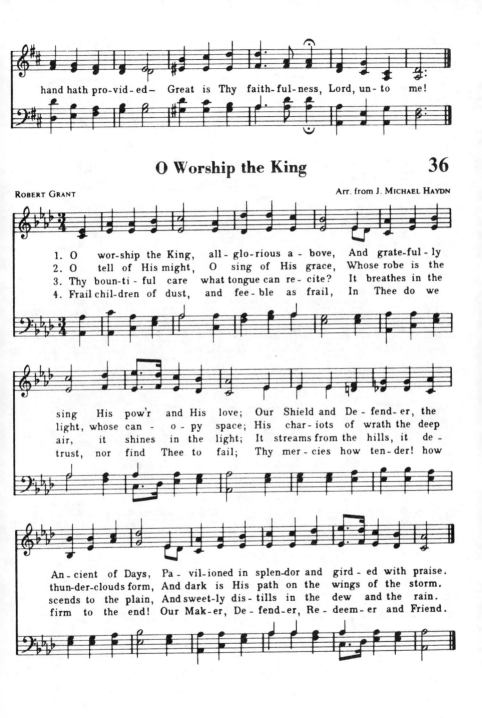

hand hath pro-vid-ed— Great is Thy faith-ful-ness, Lord, un-to me!

O Worship the King
36

Robert Grant

Arr. from J. Michael Haydn

1. O wor-ship the King, all - glo-rious a - bove, And grate-ful - ly
2. O tell of His might, O sing of His grace, Whose robe is the
3. Thy boun-ti - ful care what tongue can re - cite? It breathes in the
4. Frail chil-dren of dust, and fee - ble as frail, In Thee do we

sing His pow'r and His love; Our Shield and De - fend - er, the
light, whose can - o - py space; His char - iots of wrath the deep
air, it shines in the light; It streams from the hills, it de -
trust, nor find Thee to fail; Thy mer - cies how ten - der! how

An - cient of Days, Pa - vil-ioned in splen-dor and gird - ed with praise.
thun-der-clouds form, And dark is His path on the wings of the storm.
scends to the plain, And sweet-ly dis - tills in the dew and the rain.
firm to the end! Our Mak - er, De - fend - er, Re - deem - er and Friend.

37 Come, Thou Fount of Every Blessing

1. Come, Thou Fount of ev-'ry bless-ing, Tune my heart to sing Thy grace;
2. Here I raise mine Eb-e-ne-zer; Hith-er by Thy help I'm come;
3. O to grace how great a debt-or Dai-ly I'm con-strained to be!

Streams of mer-cy, nev-er ceas-ing, Call for songs of loud-est praise:
And I hope, by Thy good plea-sure, Safe-ly to ar-rive at home:
Let Thy grace, Lord, like a fet-ter, Bind my wan-d'ring heart to Thee:

Teach me some me-lo-dious son-net, Sung by flam-ing tongues a-bove;
Je-sus sought me when a stran-ger, Wan-d'ring from the fold of God;
Prone to wan-der, Lord, I feel it, Prone to leave the God I love;

Praise the mount! I'm fixed up-on it, Mount of Thy re-deem-ing love.
He, to res-cue me from dan-ger, In-ter-posed His pre-cious blood.
Here's my heart, Lord, take and seal it, Seal it for Thy courts a-bove.

WORDS: Robert Robinson, 1735-1790
MUSIC: Wyeth's *Repository of Sacred Music, Part Second,* 1813

A Mighty Fortress Is Our God

38

MARTIN LUTHER
Trans. by Frederick H. Hedge

MARTIN LUTHER

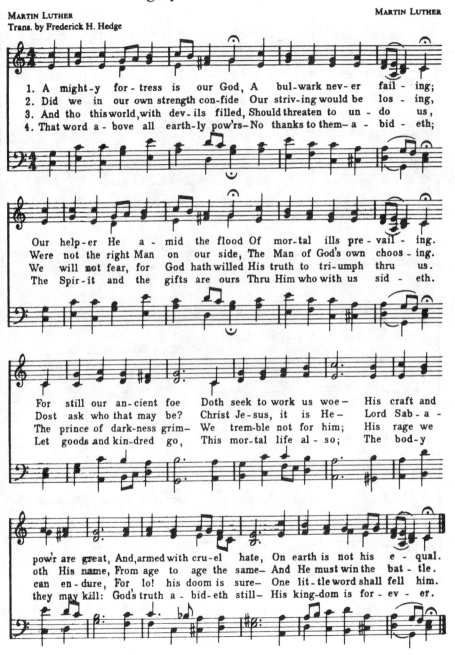

1. A might-y for-tress is our God, A bul-wark nev-er fail-ing;
2. Did we in our own strength con-fide Our striv-ing would be los-ing,
3. And tho this world, with dev-ils filled, Should threaten to un-do us,
4. That word a-bove all earth-ly pow'rs—No thanks to them a-bid-eth;

Our help-er He a-mid the flood Of mor-tal ills pre-vail-ing.
Were not the right Man on our side, The Man of God's own choos-ing.
We will not fear, for God hath willed His truth to tri-umph thru us.
The Spir-it and the gifts are ours Thru Him who with us sid-eth.

For still our an-cient foe Doth seek to work us woe— His craft and
Dost ask who that may be? Christ Je-sus, it is He— Lord Sab-a-
The prince of dark-ness grim— We trem-ble not for him; His rage we
Let goods and kin-dred go, This mor-tal life al-so; The bod-y

pow'r are great, And, armed with cru-el hate, On earth is not his e-qual.
oth His name, From age to age the same— And He must win the bat-tle.
can en-dure, For lo! his doom is sure— One lit-tle word shall fell him.
they may kill: God's truth a-bid-eth still— His king-dom is for-ev-er.

39   And Can It Be That I Should Gain?

CHARLES WESLEY   THOMAS CAMPBELL

1. And can it be that I should gain An in-t'rest in the Sav-ior's blood? Died He for me, who caused His pain? For me, who Him to death pur-sued?
2. He left His Fa-ther's throne a-bove, So free, so in-fi-ite His grace! Emp-tied Him-self of all but love, And bled for Ad-am's help-less race.
3. No con-dem-na-tion now I dread, I am my Lord's and He is mine; A-live in Him, my liv-ing Head, And clothed in right-eous-ness di-vine.

CHORUS

A-maz-ing love! How can it be That Thou, my God, shouldst die for me? A-maz-ing love! A-maz-ing love! How can it be That Thou, my God, shouldst die for me?

Our Great Savior

40

J. Wilbur Chapman

Rowland W. Prichard
Arr. by Robert Harkness

1. Je-sus! what a Friend for sin-ners! Je-sus! Lov-er of my soul;
2. Je-sus! what a Strength in weak-ness! Let me hide my-self in Him;
3. Je-sus! what a Help in sor-row! While the bil-lows o'er me roll;
4. Je-sus! what a Guide and Keep-er! While the tem-pest still is high;
5. Je-sus! I do now re-ceive Him, More than all in Him I find;

Friends may fail me, foes as-sail me, He, my Sav-ior, makes me whole.
Tempt-ed, tried, and some-times fail-ing, He, my Strength, my vic-t'ry wins.
E-ven when my heart is break-ing, He, my Com-fort, helps my soul.
Storms a-bout me, night o'er-takes me, He, my Pi-lot, hears my cry.
He hath grant-ed me for-give-ness, I am His, and He is mine.

CHORUS

Hal-le-lu-jah! what a Sav-ior! Hal-le-lu-jah! what a Friend!

Sav-ing, help-ing, keep-ing, lov-ing, He is with me to the end.

41 Rock of Ages

AUGUSTUS M. TOPLADY

THOMAS HASTINGS

1. Rock of a - ges, cleft for me, Let me hide my-self in Thee;
2. Could my tears for - ev - er flow, Could my zeal no lan-guor know,
3. While I draw this fleet-ing breath, When my eyes shall close in death,

Let the wa - ter and the blood, From Thy wound-ed side which flowed,
These for sin could not a - tone— Thou must save, and Thou a - lone:
When I rise to worlds un-known And be - hold Thee on Thy throne,

Be of sin the dou - ble cure, Save from wrath and make me pure.
In my hand no price I bring, Sim - ply to Thy cross I cling.
Rock of A - ges, cleft for me, Let me hide my-self in Thee.

42 O for a Thousand Tongues

CHARLES WESLEY

CARL G. GLÄSER
Arr. by Lowell Mason

1. O for a thou-sand tongues to sing My great Re-deem-er's praise,
2. My gra-cious Mas-ter and my God, As - sist me to pro - claim,
3. Je - sus! the name that charms our fears, That bids our sor-rows cease,
4. He breaks the pow'r of can-celed sin, He sets the pris-'ner free,
5. Hear Him, ye deaf; His praise, ye dumb, Your loos-ened tongues em-ploy;
6. Glo - ry to God and praise and love Be ev - er, ev - er giv'n

The glo - ries of my God and King, The tri-umphs of His grace.
To spread thru all the earth a-broad The hon-ors of Thy name.
'Tis mu - sic in the sin-ner's ears, 'Tis life and health and peace.
His blood can make the foul-est clean— His blood a - vailed for me.
Ye blind, be-hold your Sav - ior come; And leap, ye lame, for joy.
By saints be-low and saints a-bove— The Church in earth and heav'n.

Take the Name of Jesus with You

LYDIA BAXTER

WILLIAM H. DOANE

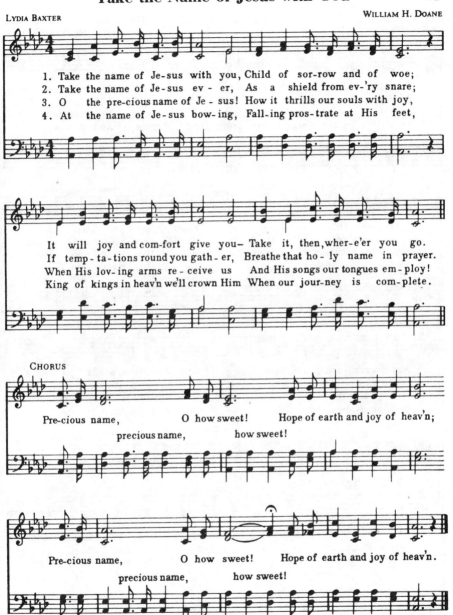

1. Take the name of Je-sus with you, Child of sor-row and of woe;
2. Take the name of Je-sus ev - er, As a shield from ev-'ry snare;
3. O the pre-cious name of Je - sus! How it thrills our souls with joy,
4. At the name of Je-sus bow-ing, Fall-ing pros-trate at His feet,

It will joy and com-fort give you— Take it, then, wher-e'er you go.
If temp - ta-tions round you gath - er, Breathe that ho - ly name in prayer.
When His lov-ing arms re - ceive us And His songs our tongues em-ploy!
King of kings in heav'n we'll crown Him When our jour-ney is com-plete.

CHORUS

Pre-cious name, O how sweet! Hope of earth and joy of heav'n;
precious name, how sweet!

Pre-cious name, O how sweet! Hope of earth and joy of heav'n.
precious name, how sweet!

44   Joy to the World!

From Psalm 98
Isaac Watts

Possibly adapted from G. F. Handel
Arr. by Lowell Mason

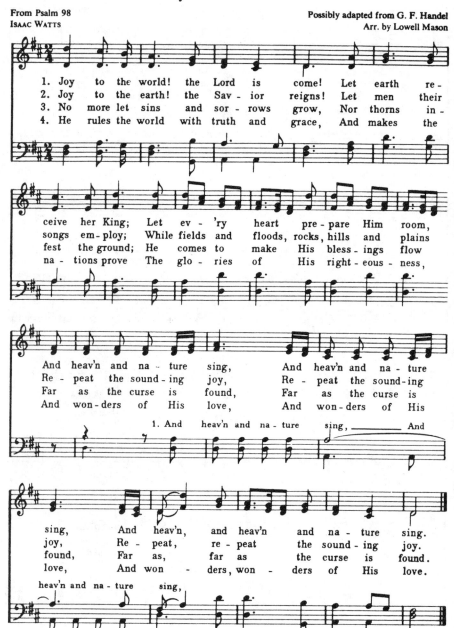

O Little Town of Bethlehem

PHILLIPS BROOKS

LEWIS H. REDNER

1. O lit - tle town of Beth-le-hem, How still we see thee lie!
2. For Christ is born of Ma - ry— And gath-ered all a - bove,
3. How si - lent - ly, how si - lent - ly The won - drous gift is giv'n!
4. O ho - ly Child of Beth-le-hem, De-scend to us, we pray;

A - bove thy deep and dream-less sleep The si - lent stars go by;
While mor-tals sleep, the an-gels keep Their watch of won-d'ring love.
So God im-parts to hu-man hearts The bless-ings of His heav'n.
Cast out our sin and en-ter in— Be born in us to - day.

Yet in thy dark streets shin - eth The ev - er - last - ing Light—
O morn-ing stars, to - geth - er Pro-claim the ho - ly birth,
No ear may hear His com - ing, But, in this world of sin,
We hear the Christ-mas an - gels The great glad ti - dings tell;

The hopes and fears of all the years Are met in thee to - night.
And prais - es sing to God the King, And peace to men on earth.
Where meek souls will re - ceive Him still The dear Christ en - ters in.
O come to us, a - bide with us, Our Lord Em-man - u - el!

O Come, All Ye Faithful

Latin hymn
Trans. by Frederick Oakeley

From Wade's *Cantus Diversi*

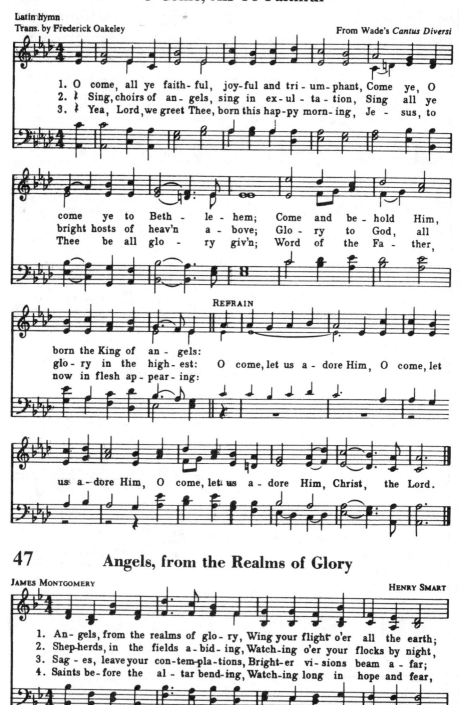

1. O come, all ye faith-ful, joy-ful and tri-um-phant, Come ye, O
2. Sing, choirs of an-gels, sing in ex-ul-ta-tion, Sing all ye
3. Yea, Lord, we greet Thee, born this hap-py morn-ing, Je-sus, to

come ye to Beth-le-hem; Come and be-hold Him,
bright hosts of heav'n a-bove; Glo-ry to God, all
Thee be all glo-ry giv'n; Word of the Fa-ther,

REFRAIN

born the King of an-gels:
glo-ry in the high-est: O come, let us a-dore Him, O come, let
now in flesh ap-pear-ing:

us a-dore Him, O come, let us a-dore Him, Christ, the Lord.

47 Angels, from the Realms of Glory

JAMES MONTGOMERY

HENRY SMART

1. An-gels, from the realms of glo-ry, Wing your flight o'er all the earth;
2. Shep-herds, in the fields a-bid-ing, Watch-ing o'er your flocks by night,
3. Sag-es, leave your con-tem-pla-tions, Bright-er vi-sions beam a-far;
4. Saints be-fore the al-tar bend-ing, Watch-ing long in hope and fear,

Ye who sang cre - a - tion's sto - ry, Now pro-claim Mes - si - ah's birth:
God with man is now re - sid - ing, Yon-der shines the in-fant Light:
Seek the great De - sire of na - tions, Ye have seen His na - tal star:
Sud-den-ly the Lord, de-scend-ing, In His tem - ple shall ap - pear:

Come and wor-ship, come and wor-ship, Wor-ship Christ, the new-born King.

Silent Night! Holy Night!

48

JOSEPH MOHR
Trans. by John F. Young

FRANZ GRÜBER.

1. Si - lent night! ho - ly night! All is calm, all is bright
2. Si - lent night! ho - ly night! Shep-herds quake at the sight;
3. Si - lent night! ho - ly night! Son of God, love's pure light

Round yon vir - gin moth-er and Child, Ho - ly In - fant, so ten-der and mild—
Glo - ries stream from heav-en a - far, Heav'n-ly hosts sing al - le - lu - ia—
Ra - diant beams from Thy ho - ly face With the dawn of re - deem-ing grace—

Sleep in heav - en - ly peace, Sleep in heav - en - ly peace.
Christ the Sav - ior is born! Christ the Sav - ior is born!
Je - sus, Lord at Thy birth, Je - sus, Lord at Thy birth.

49 Tell Me the Story of Jesus

FANNY J. CROSBY

JOHN R. SWENEY

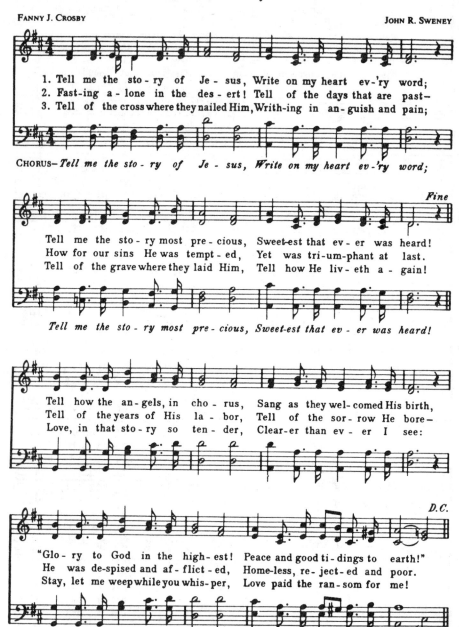

1. Tell me the sto - ry of Je - sus, Write on my heart ev-'ry word;
2. Fast-ing a - lone in the des - ert! Tell of the days that are past—
3. Tell of the cross where they nailed Him, Writh-ing in an-guish and pain;

CHORUS—*Tell me the sto - ry of Je - sus, Write on my heart ev-'ry word;*

Tell me the sto - ry most pre - cious, Sweet-est that ev - er was heard!
How for our sins He was tempt - ed, Yet was tri-um-phant at last.
Tell of the grave where they laid Him, Tell how He liv-eth a - gain!

Tell me the sto - ry most pre - cious, Sweet-est that ev - er was heard!

Tell how the an - gels, in cho - rus, Sang as they wel-comed His birth,
Tell of the years of His la - bor, Tell of the sor - row He bore—
Love, in that sto - ry so ten - der, Clear-er than ev - er I see:

"Glo - ry to God in the high - est! Peace and good ti - dings to earth!"
He was de-spised and af - flict - ed, Home-less, re - ject - ed and poor.
Stay, let me weep while you whis - per, Love paid the ran - som for me!

When I Survey the Wondrous Cross 50

From a Gregorian Chant
Arr. by Lowell Mason

ISAAC WATTS

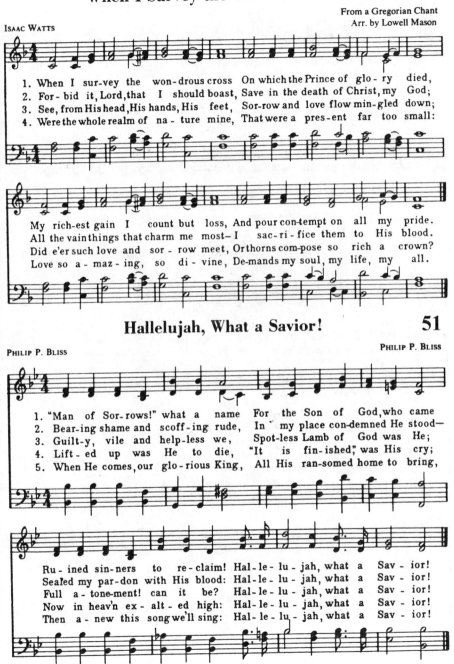

1. When I sur-vey the won-drous cross On which the Prince of glo-ry died,
2. For-bid it, Lord, that I should boast, Save in the death of Christ, my God;
3. See, from His head, His hands, His feet, Sor-row and love flow min-gled down;
4. Were the whole realm of na-ture mine, That were a pres-ent far too small:

My rich-est gain I count but loss, And pour con-tempt on all my pride.
All the vain things that charm me most—I sac-ri-fice them to His blood.
Did e'er such love and sor-row meet, Or thorns com-pose so rich a crown?
Love so a-maz-ing, so di-vine, De-mands my soul, my life, my all.

Hallelujah, What a Savior! 51

PHILIP P. BLISS

PHILIP P. BLISS

1. "Man of Sor-rows!" what a name For the Son of God, who came
2. Bear-ing shame and scoff-ing rude, In my place con-demned He stood—
3. Guilt-y, vile and help-less we, Spot-less Lamb of God was He;
4. Lift-ed up was He to die, "It is fin-ished," was His cry;
5. When He comes, our glo-rious King, All His ran-somed home to bring,

Ru-ined sin-ners to re-claim! Hal-le-lu-jah, what a Sav-ior!
Sealed my par-don with His blood: Hal-le-lu-jah, what a Sav-ior!
Full a-tone-ment! can it be? Hal-le-lu-jah, what a Sav-ior!
Now in heav'n ex-alt-ed high: Hal-le-lu-jah, what a Sav-ior!
Then a-new this song we'll sing: Hal-le-lu-jah, what a Sav-ior!

52 He Lives

ALFRED H. ACKLEY

ALFRED H. ACKLEY

1. I serve a ris-en Sav-ior, He's in the world to-day; I know that He is
2. In all the world a-round me I see His lov-ing care, And tho my heart grows
3. Re-joice, re-joice, O Chris-tian, lift up your voice and sing E - ter-nal hal - le -

liv-ing, what-ev-er men may say; I see His hand of mer-cy, I
wea-ry I nev-er will de-spair; I know that He is lead-ing thru
lu-jahs to Je-sus Christ the King! The hope of all who seek Him, the

hear His voice of cheer, And just the time I need Him He's al-ways near.
all the storm-y blast, The day of His ap-pear-ing will come at last.
help of all who find, None oth-er is so lov-ing, so good and kind.

CHORUS

He lives, He lives, Christ Je-sus lives to-day! He walks with me and
He lives, He lives,

talks with me a-long life's nar-row way. He lives, He lives, sal-
He lives, He lives,

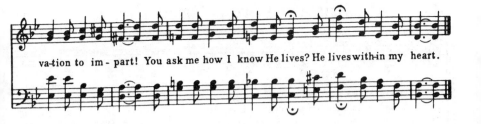

va-tion to im - part! You ask me how I know He lives? He lives with-in my heart.

Like a River Glorious 53

1. Like a riv - er glo-rious Is God's per-fect peace, O - ver all vic - to-rious
2. Hid-den in the hol-low Of His bless-ed hand, Nev - er foe can fol-low,
3. Ev - 'ry joy or tri - al Fall-eth from a - bove, Traced up-on our di - al

In its bright in - crease. Per-fect, yet it flow-eth Full-er ev - 'ry day;
Nev - er trai - tor stand. Not a surge of wor-ry, Not a shade of care,
By the Sun of Love. We may trust Him ful - ly All for us to do;

Refrain

Per - fect, yet it grow-eth Deep - er all the way.
Not a blast of hur - ry– Touch the Spir - it there. Stayed up-on Je - ho-vah,
They who trust Him whol-ly Find Him whol-ly true.

Hearts are ful - ly blest– Find-ing, as He prom-ised, Per - fect peace and rest.

WORDS: Frances R. Havergal, 1874
MUSIC: James Mountain, 1876

54   Christ the Lord Is Risen Today

1. Christ the Lord is ris'n to-day. Al - le - lu - ia!
2. Lives a-gain our glo-rious King. Al - le - lu - ia!
3. Love's re-deem-ing work is done. Al - le - lu - ia!
4. Soar we now where Christ has led. Al - le - lu - ia!

Sons of men and an-gels say: Al - le - lu - ia!
Where, O death, is now thy sting? Al - le - lu - ia!
Fought the fight, the bat-tle won. Al - le - lu - ia!
Fol-l'wing our ex-alt-ed Head. Al - le - lu - ia!

Raise your joys and tri-umphs high. Al - le - lu - ia!
Dy - ing once, He all doth save. Al - le - lu - ia!
Death in vain for-bids Him rise. Al - le - lu - ia!
Made like Him, like Him we rise. Al - le - lu - ia!

Sing, ye heav'ns, and earth, re-ply: Al - le - lu - ia!
Where thy vic-to-ry, O grave? Al - le - lu - ia!
Christ has o-pened par-a-dise. Al - le - lu - ia!
Ours the cross, the grave, the skies. Al - le - lu - ia!

TEXT: Charles Wesley
MUSIC: *Lyra Davidica*, 1708; Last stanza setting and Choral ending by Don Hart

Christ Arose

1. Low in the grave He lay— Je-sus, my Sav-ior! Wait-ing the coming day— Je-sus, my Lord!
2. Vain-ly they watch His bed— Je-sus, my Sav-ior! Vain-ly they seal the dead— Je-sus, my Lord!
3. Death can-not keep his prey— Je-sus, my Sav-ior! He tore the bars a-way— Je-sus, my Lord!

Refrain
faster

Up from the grave He a-rose, With a mighty triumph o'er His foes. He a-rose a Victor from the dark domain, And He lives for-ev-er with His saints to reign. He a-rose! He a-rose! Hal-le-lu-jah! Christ a-rose!

He a-rose, He a-rose! He a-rose!

rit.

WORDS and MUSIC: Robert Lowry, 1874

56 At the Cross

Isaac Watts
Chorus — Ralph E. Hudson

RALPH E. HUDSON

1. A - las! and did my Sav - ior bleed? And did my Sov-'reign die?
2. Was it for crimes that I have done He groaned up - on the tree?
3. Well might the sun in dark-ness hide And shut his glo - ries in,
4. But drops of grief can ne'er re - pay The debt of love I owe:

Would He de - vote that sa - cred head For such a worm as I?
A - maz-ing pit - y! grace un-known! And love be - yond de - gree!
When Christ, the might - y Mak - er, died For man the crea - ture's sin.
Here, Lord, I give my - self a - way— 'Tis all that I can do!

CHORUS

At the cross, at the cross where I first saw the light, And the

bur-den of my heart rolled a - way—
rolled a - way—
It was there by faith

I re - ceived my sight, And now I am hap-py all the day!

Jesus Shall Reign 57

ISAAC WATTS

JOHN HATTON

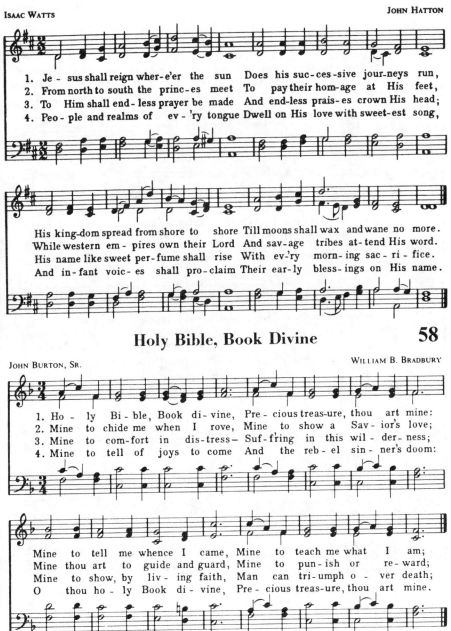

1. Je - sus shall reign wher-e'er the sun Does his suc-ces-sive jour-neys run,
2. From north to south the princ-es meet To pay their hom-age at His feet,
3. To Him shall end-less prayer be made And end-less prais-es crown His head;
4. Peo - ple and realms of ev - 'ry tongue Dwell on His love with sweet-est song,

His king-dom spread from shore to shore Till moons shall wax and wane no more.
While western em - pires own their Lord And sav-age tribes at-tend His word.
His name like sweet per-fume shall rise With ev-'ry morn-ing sac - ri - fice.
And in-fant voic - es shall pro-claim Their ear-ly bless-ings on His name.

Holy Bible, Book Divine 58

JOHN BURTON, SR.

WILLIAM B. BRADBURY

1. Ho - ly Bi - ble, Book di - vine, Pre - cious treas-ure, thou art mine:
2. Mine to chide me when I rove, Mine to show a Sav - ior's love;
3. Mine to com-fort in dis-tress— Suf-f'ring in this wil - der - ness;
4. Mine to tell of joys to come And the reb - el sin - ner's doom:

Mine to tell me whence I came, Mine to teach me what I am;
Mine thou art to guide and guard, Mine to pun - ish or re - ward;
Mine to show, by liv - ing faith, Man can tri - umph o - ver death;
O thou ho - ly Book di - vine, Pre - cious treas-ure, thou art mine.

59

When We See Christ

Esther Kerr Rusthoi   Esther Kerr Rusthoi

1. Oft - times the day seems long, our tri - als hard to bear, We're tempt-ed
2. Some-times the sky looks dark with not a ray of light, We're tossed and
3. Life's day will soon be o'er, all storms for-ev - er past, We'll cross the

to com-plain, to mur-mur and de - spair; But Christ will soon ap-pear
driv-en on, no hu-man help in sight; But there is one in heav'n
great di - vide to glo-ry, safe at last; We'll share the joys of heav'n—

to catch His Bride a - way, All tears for-ev - er o - ver in
who knows our deep-est care, Let Je - sus solve your prob-lem— just
a harp, a home, a crown, The tempt-er will be ban-ished, we'll

CHORUS

God's e - ter-nal day.
go to Him in pray'r. It will be worth it all when we see Je - sus,
lay our bur-den down.

Life's trials will seem so small when we see Christ; One glimpse of His dear face

all sor-row will e-rase, So brave-ly run the race till we see Christ.

Jesus Paid It All

60

Elvina M. Hall

John T. Grape

1. I hear the Sav-ior say, "Thy strength in-deed is small! Child of weak-ness,
2. Lord, now in-deed I find Thy pow'r, and Thine a-lone, Can change the
3. For noth-ing good have I Where-by Thy grace to claim— I'll wash my
4. And when be-fore the throne I stand in Him com-plete, "Je-sus died my

watch and pray, Find in Me thine all in all."
lep-er's spots And melt the heart of stone.
gar-ments white In the blood of Cal-v'ry's Lamb.
soul to save," My lips shall still re-peat.

CHORUS

Je-sus paid it all, All to Him I owe; Sin had left a crim-son stain— He washed it white as snow.

61 Jesus Is Coming Again

John W. Peterson

John W. Peterson

1. Mar-vel-ous mes-sage we bring, Glo-ri-ous car-ol we sing,
2. For-est and flow-er ex-claim, Moun-tain and mead-ow the same,
3. Stand-ing be-fore Him at last, Tri-al and trou-ble all past,

Won-der-ful word of the King: Je-sus is com-ing a-gain! (a-gain!)
All earth and heav-en pro-claim: Je-sus is com-ing a-gain! (a-gain!)
Crowns at His feet we will cast: Je-sus is com-ing a-gain! (a-gain!)

CHORUS
Unison

Com-ing a-gain, Com-ing a-gain;

May-be morn-ing, may-be noon, May-be eve-ning and may-be soon!

Com-ing a-gain, Com-ing a-gain;

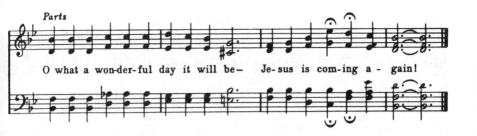

O what a won-der-ful day it will be— Je-sus is com-ing a-gain!

Faith of Our Fathers 62

FREDERICK W. FABER

HENRI F. HEMY
Adapted by James G. Walton

1. Faith of our fa-thers, liv-ing still In spite of dun-geon, fire and sword—
2. Our fa-thers, chained in pris-ons dark, Were still in heart and con-science free;
3. Faith of our fa-thers, we will love Both friend and foe in all our strife;

O how our hearts beat high with joy When-e'er we hear that glo-rious word!
How sweet would be their chil-dren's fate If they, like them, could die for thee!
And preach thee too, as love knows how, By kind-ly words and vir-tuous life.

Faith of our fa-thers, ho-ly faith, We will be true to thee till death!

63 Standing on the Promises

R. Kelso Carter

R. Kelso Carter

1. Stand-ing on the prom-is-es of Christ my King, Thru e-ter-nal
2. Stand-ing on the prom-is-es that can-not fail, When the howl-ing
3. Stand-ing on the prom-is-es of Christ the Lord, Bound to Him e-
4. Stand-ing on the prom-is-es I can-not fall, Lis-t'ning ev-'ry

a-ges let His prais-es ring; Glo-ry in the high-est I will
storms of doubt and fear as-sail, By the liv-ing word of God I
ter-nal-ly by love's strong cord, O-ver-com-ing dai-ly with the
mo-ment to the Spir-it's call, Rest-ing in my Sav-ior as my

CHORUS

shout and sing, Stand-ing on the prom-is-es of God.
shall pre-vail, Stand-ing on the prom-is-es of God. Stand - -
Spir-it's sword, Stand-ing on the prom-is-es of God. Stand-ing on the
all in all, Stand-ing on the prom-is-es of God.

ing, stand - - ing, Stand-ing on the
prom-is-es, stand-ing on the prom-is-es,

prom-is-es of God my Sav-ior; Stand - - ing,
Stand-ing on the prom-is-es,

standing, I'm standing on the prom-is-es of God.
standing on the prom-is-es,

Break Thou the Bread of Life   64

MARY ANN LATHBURY

WILLIAM F. SHERWIN

1. Break Thou the bread of life, Dear Lord, to me, As Thou didst
2. Bless Thou the truth, dear Lord, To me — to me, As Thou didst
3. Thou art the bread of life, O Lord, to me; Thy ho - ly
4. O send Thy Spir - it, Lord, Now un - to me, That He may

break the loaves Be - side the sea: Be - yond the sa - cred page
bless the bread By Gal - i - lee: Then shall all bond-age cease,
Word the truth That sav - eth me: Give me to eat and live
touch my eyes And make me see: Show me the truth con-cealed

I seek Thee, Lord; My spir - it pants for Thee, O liv - ing Word.
All fet - ters fall, And I shall find my peace, My All in all.
With Thee a - bove; Teach me to love Thy truth, For Thou art love.
With - in Thy Word, And in Thy book re - vealed I see the Lord.

65 There Is Power in the Blood

LEWIS E. JONES

LEWIS E. JONES

1. Would you be free from the bur-den of sin? There's pow'r in the blood,
2. Would you be free from your pas-sion and pride? There's pow'r in the blood,
3. Would you be whit-er, much whit-er than snow? There's pow'r in the blood,
4. Would you do serv-ice for Je-sus your King? There's pow'r in the blood,

pow'r in the blood; Would you o'er e-vil a vic-to-ry win? There's
pow'r in the blood; Come for a cleans-ing to Cal-va-ry's tide— There's
pow'r in the blood; Sin-stains are lost in its life-giv-ing flow— There's
pow'r in the blood; Would you live dai-ly His prais-es to sing? There's

CHORUS

won-der-ful pow'r in the blood. There is pow'r, pow'r, won-der-
there is

work-ing pow'r In the blood of the Lamb; There is
In the blood of the Lamb;

pow'r, pow'r, won-der-working pow'r In the pre-cious blood of the Lamb.
there is

In Times Like These

RUTH CAYE JONES   RUTH CAYE JONES

1. In times like these you need a Sav-ior, In times like these you need an
2. In times like these you need the Bi - ble, In times like these O be not
3. In times like these I have a Sav-ior, In times like these I have an

an - chor; Be ver-y sure, be ver-y sure Your an-chor holds
i - dle; Be ver-y sure, be ver-y sure Your an-chor holds
an - chor; I'm ver-y sure, I'm ver-y sure My an-chor holds

REFRAIN

and grips the Sol- id Rock! This Rock is Je - sus, Yes, He's the

One; This Rock is Je - sus, The on - ly One! 1,2. Be ver-y sure,
                                            3. I'm ver-y sure,

be ver-y sure Your an-chor holds and grips the Sol-id Rock!
I'm ver-y sure My an-chor holds and grips the Sol-id Rock!

67   **Turn Your Eyes upon Jesus**

Helen H. Lemmel   Helen H. Lemmel

1. O soul, are you wea-ry and trou - bled? No light in the
2. Thru death in-to life ev-er - last - ing He passed, and we
3. His word shall not fail you— He prom - ised; Be - lieve Him, and

dark-ness you see? There's light for a look at the Sav - ior, And
fol-low Him there; O-ver us sin no more hath do - min - ion— For
all will be well: Then go to a world that is dy - ing, His

life more a-bun-dant and free!
more than con-q'rors we are!   *CHORUS*   Turn your eyes up-on Je - sus,
per-fect sal-va-tion to tell!

Look full in His won-der-ful face, _____ And the things of
won-der-ful face,

earth will grow strange-ly dim In the light of His glo - ry and grace.

O Happy Day!

68

Philip Doddridge

Edward F. Rimbault

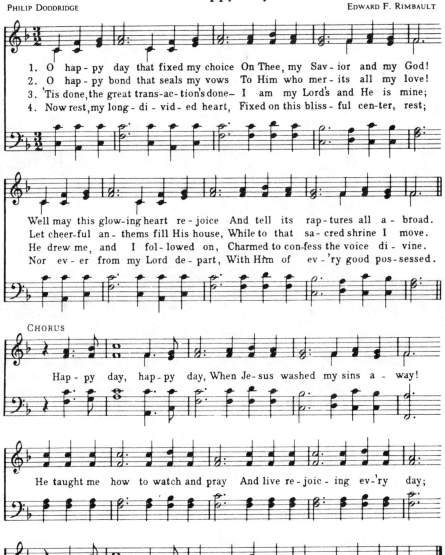

1. O hap-py day that fixed my choice On Thee, my Sav-ior and my God!
2. O hap-py bond that seals my vows To Him who mer-its all my love!
3. 'Tis done, the great trans-ac-tion's done— I am my Lord's and He is mine;
4. Now rest, my long-di-vid-ed heart, Fixed on this bliss-ful cen-ter, rest;

Well may this glow-ing heart re-joice And tell its rap-tures all a-broad.
Let cheer-ful an-thems fill His house, While to that sa-cred shrine I move.
He drew me, and I fol-lowed on, Charmed to con-fess the voice di-vine.
Nor ev-er from my Lord de-part, With Him of ev-'ry good pos-sessed.

CHORUS

Hap-py day, hap-py day, When Je-sus washed my sins a-way!

He taught me how to watch and pray And live re-joic-ing ev-'ry day;

Hap-py day, hap-py day, When Je-sus washed my sins a-way!

69 There Is a Fountain

WILLIAM COWPER

American melody

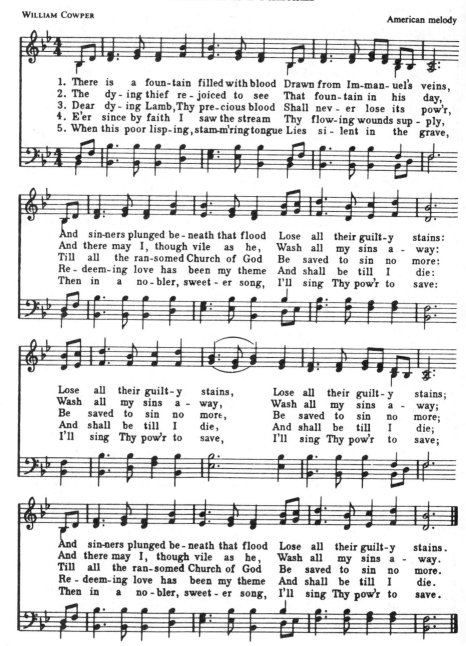

1. There is a foun-tain filled with blood Drawn from Im-man-uel's veins,
2. The dy-ing thief re-joiced to see That foun-tain in his day,
3. Dear dy-ing Lamb, Thy pre-cious blood Shall nev-er lose its pow'r,
4. E'er since by faith I saw the stream Thy flow-ing wounds sup-ply,
5. When this poor lisp-ing, stam-m'ring tongue Lies si-lent in the grave,

And sin-ners plunged be-neath that flood Lose all their guilt-y stains:
And there may I, though vile as he, Wash all my sins a-way:
Till all the ran-somed Church of God Be saved to sin no more:
Re-deem-ing love has been my theme And shall be till I die:
Then in a no-bler, sweet-er song, I'll sing Thy pow'r to save:

Lose all their guilt-y stains, Lose all their guilt-y stains;
Wash all my sins a-way, Wash all my sins a-way;
Be saved to sin no more, Be saved to sin no more;
And shall be till I die, And shall be till I die;
I'll sing Thy pow'r to save, I'll sing Thy pow'r to save;

And sin-ners plunged be-neath that flood Lose all their guilt-y stains.
And there may I, though vile as he, Wash all my sins a-way.
Till all the ran-somed Church of God Be saved to sin no more.
Re-deem-ing love has been my theme And shall be till I die.
Then in a no-bler, sweet-er song, I'll sing Thy pow'r to save.

I Know Whom I Have Believed

70

Daniel W. Whittle

James McGranahan

1. I know not why God's won-drous grace To me He hath made known,
2. I know not how this sav-ing faith To me He did im - part,
3. I know not how the Spir-it moves, Con-vinc-ing men of sin,
4. I know not what of good or ill May be re-served for me,
5. I know not when my Lord may come— At night or noon-day fair,

Nor why, un-wor-thy, Christ in love Re-deemed me for His own.
Nor how be-liev-ing in His Word Wrought peace with-in my heart.
Re-veal-ing Je-sus thru the Word, Cre-at-ing faith in Him.
Of wea-ry ways or gold-en days Be-fore His face I see.
Nor if I'll walk the vale with Him Or meet Him in the air.

CHORUS

But "I know whom I have be-liev-ed, And am per-suad-ed that He is

a-ble To keep that which I've com-mit-ted Un-to Him a-gainst that day."

Saved, Saved

Unison

1. I've found a friend who is all to me, His
2. He saves me from ev-'ry sin and harm, Se-
3. When poor and need - y and all a - lone, In

love is ev - er true; I love to tell how He
cures my soul each day; I'm lean - ing strong on His
love He said to me, "Come un - to Me and I'll

lift - ed me, And what His grace can do for you.
might - y arm; I know He'll guide me all the way.
lead you home, To live with Me e - ter - nal - ly."

Parts

Saved by His pow'r di-vine, Saved to new life sub-lime!
Saved by His pow'r, Saved to new life,

Life now is sweet and my joy is com-plete, For I'm saved, saved, saved!

WORDS: Jack P. Scholfield
MUSIC: Jack P. Scholfield

Tell Me the Old, Old Story

A. CATHERINE HANKEY

WILLIAM H. DOANE

1. Tell me the old, old sto-ry Of un-seen things a-bove, Of Je-sus
2. Tell me the sto-ry slow-ly, That I may take it in— That won-der-
3. Tell me the sto-ry soft-ly, With ear-nest tones and grave; Re-mem-ber,
4. Tell me the same old sto-ry When you have cause to fear That this world's

and His glo-ry, Of Je-sus and His love. Tell me the sto-ry
ful re-demp-tion, God's rem-e-dy for sin. Tell me the sto-ry
I'm the sin-ner Whom Je-sus came to save. Tell me the sto-ry
emp-ty glo-ry Is cost-ing me too dear. Yes, and when that world's

sim-ply, As to a lit-tle child, For I am weak and wea-ry,
oft-en, For I for-get so soon; The ear-ly dew of morn-ing
al-ways, If you would real-ly be, In an-y time of trou-ble,
glo-ry Is dawn-ing on my soul, Tell me the old, old sto-ry:

CHORUS

And help-less and de-filed. Tell me the old, old sto-ry, Tell me the
Has passed a-way at noon.
A com-fort-er to me.
"Christ Je-sus makes thee whole."

old, old sto-ry, Tell me the old, old sto-ry Of Je-sus and His love.

73   Jesus Saves!

PRISCILLA J. OWENS

WILLIAM J. KIRKPATRICK

1. We have heard the joy-ful sound— Je-sus saves! Je-sus saves!
2. Waft it on the roll-ing tide— Je-sus saves! Je-sus saves!
3. Sing a-bove the bat-tle strife— Je-sus saves! Je-sus saves!
4. Give the winds a might-y voice— Je-sus saves! Je-sus saves!

Spread the ti-dings all a-round— Je-sus saves! Je-sus saves!
Tell to sin-ners far and wide— Je-sus saves! Je-sus saves!
By His death and end-less life— Je-sus saves! Je-sus saves!
Let the na-tions now re-joice— Je-sus saves! Je-sus saves!

Bear the news to ev-'ry land, Climb the steeps and cross the waves;
Sing, ye is-lands of the sea! Ech-o back, ye o-cean caves!
Sing it soft-ly thru the gloom, When the heart for mer-cy craves;
Shout sal-va-tion full and free, High-est hills and deep-est caves;

On-ward! 'tis our Lord's com-mand— Je-sus saves! Je-sus saves!
Earth shall keep her ju-bi-lee— Je-sus saves! Je-sus saves!
Sing in tri-umph o'er the tomb— Je-sus saves! Je-sus saves!
This our song of vic-to-ry— Je-sus saves! Je-sus saves!

Jesus, I Come

WILLIAM T. SLEEPER

GEORGE C. STEBBINS

1. Out of my bond-age, sor-row and night, Je-sus, I come, Je-sus, I come;
2. Out of my shame-ful fail-ure and loss, Je-sus, I come, Je-sus, I come;
3. Out of un-rest and ar - ro-gant pride, Je-sus, I come, Je-sus, I come;
4. Out of the fear and dread of the tomb, Je-sus, I come, Je-sus, I come;

In - to Thy free-dom, glad-ness and light, Je-sus, I come to Thee.
In - to the glo-rious gain of Thy cross, Je-sus, I come to Thee.
In - to Thy bless-ed will to a - bide, Je-sus, I come to Thee.
In - to the joy and light of Thy home, Je-sus, I come to Thee.

Out of my sick-ness in - to Thy health, Out of my want and in - to Thy wealth,
Out of earth's sorrows in - to Thy balm, Out of life's storms and in - to Thy calm,
Out of my-self to dwell in Thy love, Out of de-spair in-to rap-tures a-bove,
Out of the depths of ru - in un-told, In - to the peace of Thy shel-ter-ing fold,

Out of my sin and in - to Thy-self, Je-sus, I come to Thee.
Out of dis-tress to ju - bi-lant psalm, Je-sus, I come to Thee.
Up-ward for aye on wings like a dove, Je-sus, I come to Thee.
Ev - er Thy glo-rious face to be-hold, Je-sus, I come to Thee.

75 Amazing Grace! How Sweet the Sound

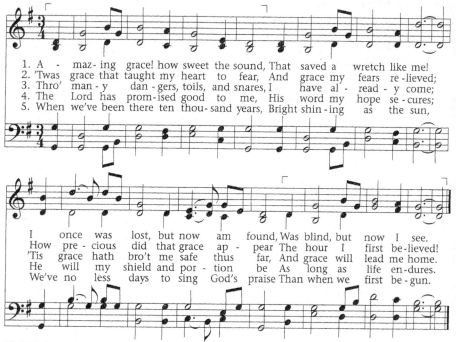

1. A - maz - ing grace! how sweet the sound, That saved a wretch like me!
2. 'Twas grace that taught my heart to fear, And grace my fears re - lieved;
3. Thro' man - y dan - gers, toils, and snares, I have al - read - y come;
4. The Lord has prom-ised good to me, His word my hope se - cures;
5. When we've been there ten thou-sand years, Bright shin-ing as the sun,

I once was lost, but now am found, Was blind, but now I see.
How pre - cious did that grace ap - pear The hour I first be - lieved!
'Tis grace hath bro't me safe thus far, And grace will lead me home.
He will my shield and por - tion be As long as life en - dures.
We've no less days to sing God's praise Than when we first be - gun.

WORDS: St. 1-4, John Newton, 1725-1807; st. 5, anonymous *c.* 1790
MUSIC: *Virginia Harmony*, 1831

76 Burdens Are Lifted at Calvary

JOHN M. MOORE   JOHN M. MOORE

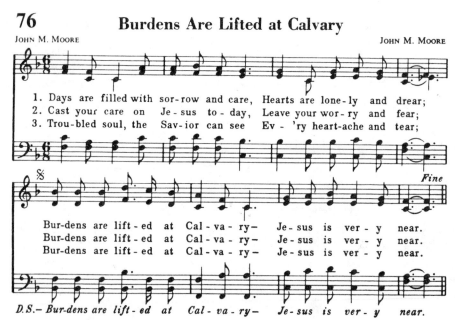

1. Days are filled with sor-row and care, Hearts are lone-ly and drear;
2. Cast your care on Je - sus to - day, Leave your wor - ry and fear;
3. Trou-bled soul, the Sav-ior can see Ev - 'ry heart-ache and tear;

Fine

Bur-dens are lift - ed at Cal-va - ry— Je-sus is ver - y near.
Bur-dens are lift - ed at Cal-va - ry— Je-sus is ver - y near.
Bur-dens are lift - ed at Cal-va - ry— Je-sus is ver - y near.

D.S.—Bur-dens are lift - ed at Cal - va - ry— Je-sus is ver - y near.

CHORUS

Bur-dens are lift-ed at Cal - va - ry, Cal - va - ry, Cal - va - ry;

Oh, How I Love Jesus 77

1. There is a name I love to hear, I love to sing its worth;
2. It tells me of a Sav-ior's love, Who died to set me free;
3. It tells me what my Fa - ther has In store for ev - 'ry day;
4. It tells of One whose lov-ing heart Can feel my deep-est woe,

It sounds as mu - sic in my ear, The sweet-est name on earth.
It tells me of His pre - cious blood, The sin - ner's per - fect plea.
And though I tread a dark-some path, Yields sun - shine all the way.
Who in each sor - row bears a part, That none can bear be - low.

Oh, how I love Je - sus, Oh, how I love Je - sus,

Oh, how I love Je - sus, Be - cause He first loved me.

WORDS: Frederick Whitfield
MUSIC: Anonymous

78 Softly and Tenderly

Will L. Thompson

Will L. Thompson

1. Soft-ly and ten-der-ly Je-sus is call-ing, Call-ing for
2. Why should we tar-ry when Je-sus is plead-ing, Plead-ing for
3. Time is now fleet-ing, the mo-ments are pass-ing, Pass-ing from
4. O for the won-der-ful love He has prom-ised, Prom-ised for

you and for me; See, on the por-tals He's wait-ing and watch-ing,
you and for me? Why should we lin-ger and heed not His mer-cies,
you and from me; Shad-ows are gath-er-ing, death-beds are com-ing,
you and for me; Tho we have sinned He has mer-cy and par-don,

CHORUS

Watch-ing for you and for me.
Mer-cies for you and for me? Come home, come home,
Com-ing for you and for me. Come home, come home,
Par-don for you and for me.

Ye who are wea-ry, come home; Ear-nest-ly,

ten-der-ly, Je-sus is call-ing— Call-ing, "O sin-ner, come home!"

Blessed Assurance

Fanny J. Crosby

Phoebe P. Knapp

1. Bless-ed as - sur - ance, Je-sus is mine! O what a fore-taste of glo - ry di - vine! Heir of sal - va - tion, pur-chase of God, Born of His Spir - it, washed in His blood.

2. Per - fect sub-mis - sion, per-fect de - light! Vi -sions of rap - ture now burst on my sight; An - gels de-scend-ing bring from a - bove Ech - oes of mer - cy, whis-pers of love.

3. Per - fect sub-mis - sion—all is at rest, I in my Sav - ior am hap - py and blest; Watch-ing and wait - ing, look-ing a - bove, Filled with His good-ness, lost in His love.

CHORUS

This is my sto - ry, this is my song, Prais-ing my Sav - ior all the day long; This is my sto - ry, this is my song, Prais-ing my Sav - ior all the day long.

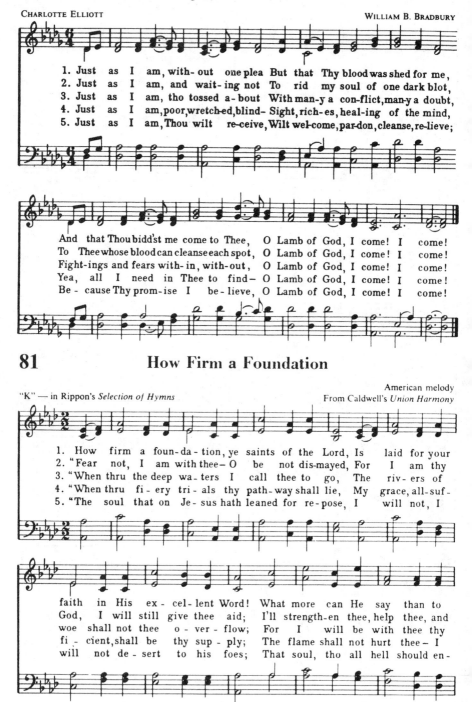

80   Just As I Am

CHARLOTTE ELLIOTT

WILLIAM B. BRADBURY

1. Just as I am, with-out one plea But that Thy blood was shed for me,
2. Just as I am, and wait-ing not To rid my soul of one dark blot,
3. Just as I am, tho tossed a-bout With man-y a con-flict, man-y a doubt,
4. Just as I am, poor, wretch-ed, blind— Sight, rich-es, heal-ing of the mind,
5. Just as I am, Thou wilt re-ceive, Wilt wel-come, par-don, cleanse, re-lieve;

And that Thou bidd'st me come to Thee, O Lamb of God, I come! I come!
To Thee whose blood can cleanse each spot, O Lamb of God, I come! I come!
Fight-ings and fears with-in, with-out, O Lamb of God, I come! I come!
Yea, all I need in Thee to find— O Lamb of God, I come! I come!
Be-cause Thy prom-ise I be-lieve, O Lamb of God, I come! I come!

81   How Firm a Foundation

"K" — in Rippon's *Selection of Hymns*

American melody
From Caldwell's *Union Harmony*

1. How firm a foun-da-tion, ye saints of the Lord, Is laid for your
2. "Fear not, I am with thee— O be not dis-mayed, For I am thy
3. "When thru the deep wa-ters I call thee to go, The riv-ers of
4. "When thru fi-er-y tri-als thy path-way shall lie, My grace, all-suf-
5. "The soul that on Je-sus hath leaned for re-pose, I will not, I

faith in His ex-cel-lent Word! What more can He say than to
God, I will still give thee aid; I'll strength-en thee, help thee, and
woe shall not thee o-ver-flow; For I will be with thee thy
fi-cient, shall be thy sup-ply; The flame shall not hurt thee—I
will not de-sert to his foes; That soul, tho all hell should en-

you He hath said— To you, who for ref-uge to Je-sus have fled?
cause thee to stand, Up-held by my gra-cious, om-nip-o-tent hand.
trou-bles to bless, And sanc-ti-fy to thee thy deep-est dis-tress.
on-ly de-sign Thy dross to con-sume and thy gold to re-fine.
deav-or to shake, I'll nev-er— no, nev-er— no, nev-er for-sake!"

Only Trust Him 82

JOHN H. STOCKTON

JOHN H. STOCKTON

1. Come, ev-'ry soul by sin op-pressed—There's mer-cy with the Lord,
2. For Je-sus shed His pre-cious blood—Rich bless-ings to be-stow;
3. Yes, Je-sus is the Truth, the Way, That leads you in-to rest;

And He will sure-ly give you rest By trust-ing in His word.
Plunge now in-to the crim-son flood That wash-es white as snow.
Be-lieve in Him with-out de-lay And you are ful-ly blest.

CHORUS

On-ly trust Him, on-ly trust Him, On-ly trust Him now;
He will save you, He will save you, He will save you now.

83 It Is Well with My Soul

HORATIO G. SPAFFORD

PHILIP P. BLISS

1. When peace, like a riv-er, at-tend-eth my way, When sor-rows like
2. Tho Sa-tan should buf-fet, tho tri-als should come, Let this blest as-
3. My sin— O the bliss of this glo-ri-ous tho't— My sin, not in
4. And, Lord, haste the day when my faith shall be sight, The clouds be rolled

sea-bil-lows roll— What-ev-er my lot, Thou hast taught me to say,
sur-ance con-trol, That Christ hath re-gard-ed my help-less es-tate,
part, but the whole, Is nailed to the cross, and I bear it no more:
back as a scroll: The trump shall re-sound and the Lord shall de-scend,

CHORUS

It is well, it is well with my soul. It is well
And hath shed His own blood for my soul.
Praise the Lord, praise the Lord, O my soul! It is well
"E-ven so"— it is well with my soul.

with my soul, It is well, it is well with my soul.
with my soul,

'Tis So Sweet to Trust in Jesus

LOUISA M. R. STEAD

WILLIAM J. KIRKPATRICK

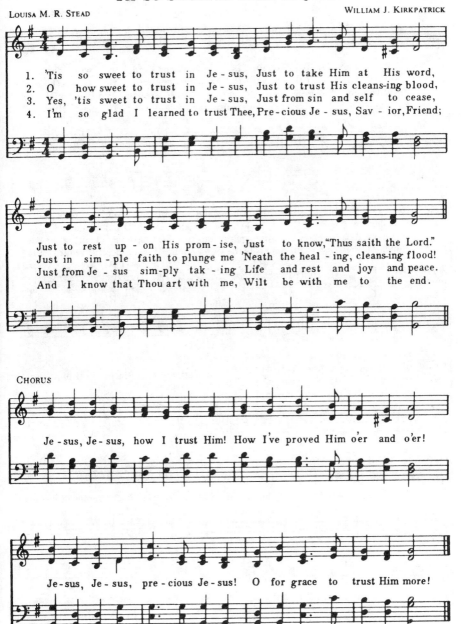

1. 'Tis so sweet to trust in Je-sus, Just to take Him at His word,
2. O how sweet to trust in Je-sus, Just to trust His cleans-ing blood,
3. Yes, 'tis sweet to trust in Je-sus, Just from sin and self to cease,
4. I'm so glad I learned to trust Thee, Pre-cious Je-sus, Sav-ior, Friend;

Just to rest up-on His prom-ise, Just to know, "Thus saith the Lord."
Just in sim-ple faith to plunge me 'Neath the heal-ing, cleans-ing flood!
Just from Je-sus sim-ply tak-ing Life and rest and joy and peace.
And I know that Thou art with me, Wilt be with me to the end.

CHORUS

Je-sus, Je-sus, how I trust Him! How I've proved Him o'er and o'er!

Je-sus, Je-sus, pre-cious Je-sus! O for grace to trust Him more!

85 He Hideth My Soul

FANNY J. CROSBY

WILLIAM J. KIRKPATRICK

1. A won-der-ful Sav-ior is Je-sus my Lord, A won-der-ful Sav-ior to me; He hid-eth my soul in the cleft of the rock, Where riv-ers of pleas-ure I see.

2. A won-der-ful Sav-ior is Je-sus my Lord— He tak-eth my bur-den a-way; He hold-eth me up and I shall not be moved, He giv-eth me strength as my day.

3. With num-ber-less bless-ings each mo-ment He crowns, And, filled with His full-ness di-vine, I sing in my rap-ture, "O glo-ry to God For such a Re-deem-er as mine!"

4. When clothed in His brightness trans-port-ed I rise To meet Him in clouds of the sky, His per-fect sal-va-tion, His won-der-ful love, I'll shout with the mil-lions on high.

CHORUS

He hid-eth my soul in the cleft of the rock That shadows a dry, thirsty land; He hid-eth my life in the depths of His love, And cov-ers me there with His hand, And cov-ers me there with His hand.

Trust and Obey

JOHN H. SAMMIS

DANIEL B. TOWNER

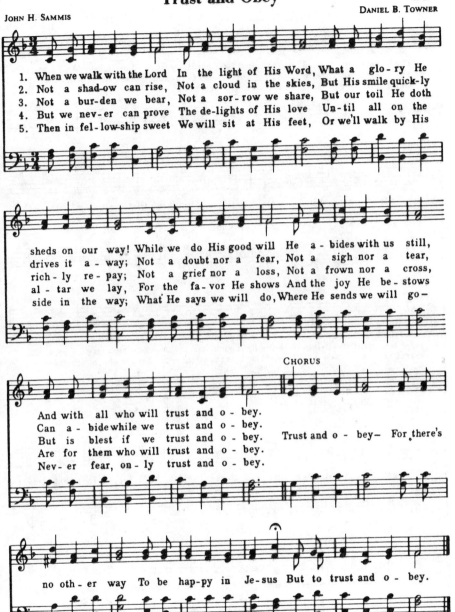

1. When we walk with the Lord In the light of His Word, What a glo-ry He
2. Not a shad-ow can rise, Not a cloud in the skies, But His smile quick-ly
3. Not a bur-den we bear, Not a sor-row we share, But our toil He doth
4. But we nev-er can prove The de-lights of His love Un-til all on the
5. Then in fel-low-ship sweet We will sit at His feet, Or we'll walk by His

sheds on our way! While we do His good will He a-bides with us still,
drives it a-way; Not a doubt nor a fear, Not a sigh nor a tear,
rich-ly re-pay; Not a grief nor a loss, Not a frown nor a cross,
al-tar we lay, For the fa-vor He shows And the joy He be-stows
side in the way; What He says we will do, Where He sends we will go—

CHORUS

And with all who will trust and o-bey.
Can a-bide while we trust and o-bey.
But is blest if we trust and o-bey. Trust and o-bey— For there's
Are for them who will trust and o-bey.
Nev-er fear, on-ly trust and o-bey.

no oth-er way To be hap-py in Je-sus But to trust and o-bey.

87 Mansion over the Hilltop

IRA F. STANPHILL

IRA F. STANPHILL

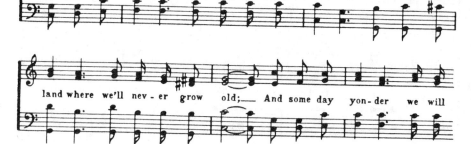

1. I'm sat - is - fied with just a cot - tage be - low,— A lit - tle
2. Tho oft - en tempt - ed, tor - ment - ed and test - ed And, like the
3. Don't think me poor or de - sert - ed or lone - ly— I'm not dis-

sil - ver and a lit - tle gold;— But in that cit - y where the
proph - et, my— pil - low a stone,— And tho I find here no—
cour - aged, I'm— heav - en - bound;— I'm just a pil - grim in—

ran - somed will shine,— I want a gold one that's sil - ver - lined.—
per - ma - nent dwell - ing, I know He'll give me a man - sion my own.—
search of a cit - y, I want a man - sion, a harp and a crown.—

Chorus

I've got a man - sion just o - ver the hill - top, In that bright

land where we'll nev - er grow old;— And some day yon - der we will

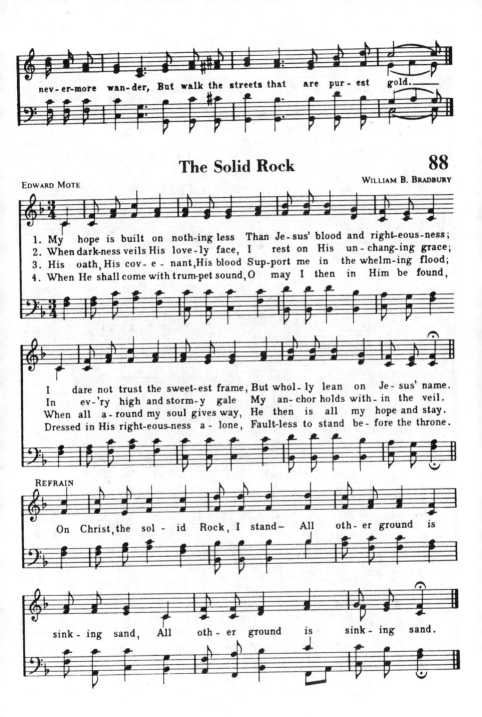

nev-er-more wan-der, But walk the streets that are pur-est gold.

The Solid Rock

88

EDWARD MOTE

WILLIAM B. BRADBURY

1. My hope is built on noth-ing less Than Je-sus' blood and right-eous-ness;
2. When dark-ness veils His love-ly face, I rest on His un-chang-ing grace;
3. His oath, His cov-e-nant, His blood Sup-port me in the whelm-ing flood;
4. When He shall come with trum-pet sound, O may I then in Him be found,

I dare not trust the sweet-est frame, But whol-ly lean on Je-sus' name.
In ev-'ry high and storm-y gale My an-chor holds with-in the veil.
When all a-round my soul gives way, He then is all my hope and stay.
Dressed in His right-eous-ness a-lone, Fault-less to stand be-fore the throne.

REFRAIN

On Christ, the sol-id Rock, I stand— All oth-er ground is sink-ing sand, All oth-er ground is sink-ing sand.

89

Moment by Moment

DANIEL W. WHITTLE

MAY WHITTLE MOODY

1. Dy-ing with Je-sus by death reck-oned mine, Liv-ing with Je-sus a
2. Nev-er a tri-al that He is not there, Nev-er a bur-den that
3. Nev-er a heart-ache and nev-er a groan, Nev-er a tear-drop and
4. Nev-er a weak-ness that He doth not feel, Nev-er a sick-ness that

new life di-vine, Look-ing to Je-sus till glo-ry doth shine—
He doth not bear; Nev-er a sor-row that He doth not share—
nev-er a moan, Nev-er a dan-ger but there on the throne,
He can-not heal; Mo-ment by mo-ment, in woe or in weal,

CHORUS

Mo-ment by mo-ment, O Lord, I am Thine.
Mo-ment by mo-ment, I'm un-der His care.
Mo-ment by mo-ment, He thinks of His own.   Mo-ment by mo-ment I'm
Je-sus, my Sav-ior, a-bides with me still.

kept in His love, Mo-ment by mo-ment I've life from a-bove; Look-ing to

Je-sus till glo-ry doth shine, Mo-ment by mo-ment, O Lord, I am Thine.

Guide Me, O Thou Great Jehovah

1. Guide me, O Thou great Je - ho - vah, Pil - grim through this
2. O - pen now the crys - tal foun - tain, Whence the heal - ing
3. When I tread the verge of Jor - dan, Bid my anx - ious

bar - ren land; I am weak, but Thou art might - y; Hold me
stream doth flow; Let the fire and cloud - y pil - lar Lead me
fears sub - side; Bear me thro' the swell - ing cur - rent, Land me

with Thy pow'r - ful hand; Bread of heav - en, Bread of heav - en,
all my jour - ney through; Strong De - liv - erer, strong De - liv - erer,
safe on Ca - naan's side; Songs of prais - es, songs of prais - es

Feed me till I want no more, Feed me till I want no more.
Be Thou still my strength and shield, Be Thou still my strength and shield.
I will ev - er give to Thee, I will ev - er give to Thee.

WORDS: William Williams
MUSIC: John Hughes

91

Surely Goodness and Mercy

JOHN W. PETERSON
and ALFRED B. SMITH

JOHN W. PETERSON
and ALFRED B. SMITH

1. A pil-grim was I; and a-wan-d'ring, In the cold night of sin I did roam, When Je-sus the kind Shep-herd found me, And now I am on my way home.
2. He re-stor-eth my soul when I'm wea-ry, He giv-eth me strength day by day; He leads me be-side the still wa-ters, He guards me each step of the way.
3. When I walk thru the dark lone-some val-ley, My Sav-ior will walk with me there; And safe-ly His great hand will lead me To the man-sions He's gone to pre-pare.

CHORUS

Sure-ly good-ness and mer-cy shall fol-low me All the days, all the days of my life; Sure-ly good-ness and mer-cy shall fol-low me All the days, all the days of my life.

Savior, Like a Shepherd Lead Us

From *Hymns for the Young*
Attr. to Dorothy A. Thrupp

WILLIAM B. BRADBURY

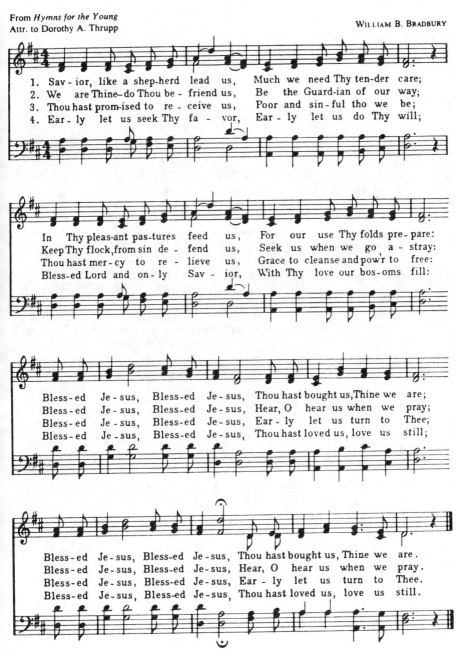

1. Sav - ior, like a shep-herd lead us, Much we need Thy ten-der care;
2. We are Thine—do Thou be - friend us, Be the Guard-ian of our way;
3. Thou hast prom-ised to re - ceive us, Poor and sin - ful tho we be;
4. Ear - ly let us seek Thy fa - vor, Ear - ly let us do Thy will;

In Thy pleas-ant pas-tures feed us, For our use Thy folds pre - pare:
Keep Thy flock, from sin de - fend us, Seek us when we go a - stray:
Thou hast mer-cy to re - lieve us, Grace to cleanse and pow'r to free:
Bless-ed Lord and on - ly Sav - ior, With Thy love our bos-oms fill:

Bless - ed Je - sus, Bless - ed Je - sus, Thou hast bought us, Thine we are;
Bless - ed Je - sus, Bless - ed Je - sus, Hear, O hear us when we pray;
Bless - ed Je - sus, Bless - ed Je - sus, Ear - ly let us turn to Thee;
Bless - ed Je - sus, Bless - ed Je - sus, Thou hast loved us, love us still;

Bless - ed Je - sus, Bless - ed Je - sus, Thou hast bought us, Thine we are.
Bless - ed Je - sus, Bless - ed Je - sus, Hear, O hear us when we pray.
Bless - ed Je - sus, Bless - ed Je - sus, Ear - ly let us turn to Thee.
Bless - ed Je - sus, Bless - ed Je - sus, Thou hast loved us, love us still.

93

Day by Day

Lina Sandell Berg
Trans. by Andrew L. Skoog

Oscar Ahnfelt

1. Day by day and with each pass-ing mo-ment, Strength I find to meet my tri-als here; Trust-ing in my Fa-ther's wise be-stow-ment, I've no cause for wor-ry or for fear. He whose heart is kind be-yond all meas-ure Gives un-to each day what He deems best— Lov-ing-ly, its part of pain and pleas-ure, Min-gling toil with peace and rest.

2. Ev-'ry day the Lord Him-self is near me With a spe-cial mer-cy for each hour; All my cares He fain would bear, and cheer me, He whose name is Coun-sel-lor and Pow'r. The pro-tec-tion of His child and treas-ure Is a charge that on Him-self He laid; "As thy days, thy strength shall be in meas-ure," This the pledge to me He made.

3. Help me then in ev-'ry trib-u-la-tion So to trust Thy prom-is-es, O Lord, That I lose not faith's sweet con-so-la-tion Of-fered me with-in Thy ho-ly word. Help me, Lord, when toil and trou-ble meet-ing, E'er to take, as from a fa-ther's hand, One by one, the days, the mo-ments fleet-ing, Till I reach the prom-ised land.

Higher Ground

Johnson Oatman, Jr.   Charles H. Gabriel

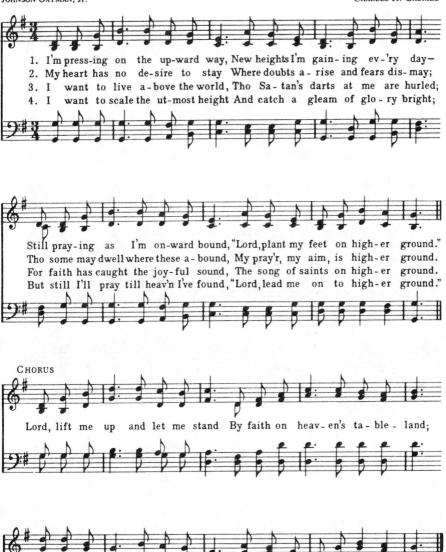

1. I'm press-ing on the up-ward way, New heights I'm gain-ing ev-'ry day—
2. My heart has no de-sire to stay Where doubts a-rise and fears dis-may;
3. I want to live a-bove the world, Tho Sa-tan's darts at me are hurled;
4. I want to scale the ut-most height And catch a gleam of glo-ry bright;

Still pray-ing as I'm on-ward bound, "Lord, plant my feet on high-er ground."
Tho some may dwell where these a-bound, My pray'r, my aim, is high-er ground.
For faith has caught the joy-ful sound, The song of saints on high-er ground.
But still I'll pray till heav'n I've found, "Lord, lead me on to high-er ground."

CHORUS

Lord, lift me up and let me stand By faith on heav-en's ta-ble-land;

A high-er plane than I have found— Lord, plant my feet on high-er ground.

95 Beneath the Cross of Jesus

ELIZABETH C. CLEPHANE

FREDERICK C. MAKER

1. Be - neath the cross of Je - sus I fain would take my stand,
2. Up - on that cross of Je - sus Mine eye at times can see
3. I take, O cross, thy shad - ow For my a - bid - ing - place —

The shad - ow of a might - y Rock With - in a wea - ry land;
The ver - y dy - ing form of One Who suf - fered there for me;
I ask no oth - er sun-shine than The sun-shine of His face;

A home with - in the wil - der - ness, A rest up - on the way
And from my smit - ten heart with tears Two won-ders I con - fess —
Con - tent to let the world go by, To know no gain nor loss,

From the burn-ing of the noon-day heat And the bur-den of the day.
The won-ders of His glo-rious love And my own worth-less-ness.
My sin - ful self my on - ly shame, My glo - ry all the cross.

There Shall Be Showers of Blessing

DANIEL W. WHITTLE

JAMES McGRANAHAN

1. "There shall be show-ers of bless-ing"– This is the prom-ise of love;
2. "There shall be show-ers of bless-ing"– Pre-cious re-viv-ing a-gain;
3. "There shall be show-ers of bless-ing"– Send them up-on us, O Lord;
4. "There shall be show-ers of bless-ing"– O that to-day they might fall,

There shall be sea-sons re-fresh-ing, Sent from the Sav-ior a-bove.
O-ver the hills and the val-leys Sound of a-bun-dance of rain.
Grant to us now a re-fresh-ing, Come and now hon-or Thy Word.
Now as to God we're con-fess-ing, Now as on Je-sus we call!

CHORUS

Show-ers of bless-ing, Show-ers of bless-ing we need;
Show-ers, show-ers of bless-ing,

Mer-cy-drops round us are fall-ing, But for the show-ers we plead.

97

More Love to Thee

ELIZABETH PRENTISS

WILLIAM H. DOANE

1. More love to Thee, O Christ, More love to Thee! Hear Thou the
2. Once earth-ly joy I craved, Sought peace and rest; Now Thee a-
3. Let sor-row do its work, Send grief and pain; Sweet are Thy
4. Then shall my lat-est breath Whis-per Thy praise; This be the

prayer I make On bend-ed knee; This is my ear-nest plea:
lone I seek— Give what is best; This all my prayer shall be:
mes- sen-gers, Sweet their re-frain, When they can sing with me,
part-ing cry My heart shall raise; This still its prayer shall be:

More love, O Christ, to Thee, More love to Thee, More love to Thee!

98

Thank You, Lord

SETH SYKES
and BESSIE SYKES

SETH SYKES
and BESSIE SYKES

1. Some thank the Lord for friends and home, For mer-cies sure and sweet;
2. Some thank Him for the flow'rs that grow, Some for the stars that shine;
3. I trust in Him from day to day, I prove His sav-ing grace;

But I would praise Him for His grace— In prayer I would re-peat:
My heart is filled with joy and praise Be-cause I know He's mine.
I'll sing this song of praise to Him Un-til I see His face.

Thank you, Lord, for sav-ing my soul, Thank you, Lord, for mak-ing me whole;

Thank you, Lord, for giv-ing to me Thy great sal-va-tion so rich and free.

I Need Thee Every Hour 99

ANNIE S. HAWKS
Chorus — Robert Lowry

ROBERT LOWRY

1. I need Thee ev-'ry hour, Most gra-cious Lord; No ten-der voice like
2. I need Thee ev-'ry hour, Stay Thou near by; Temp-ta-tions lose their
3. I need Thee ev-'ry hour, In joy or pain; Come quick-ly and a-
4. I need Thee ev-'ry hour, Most Ho-ly One; O make me Thine in-

CHORUS

Thine Can peace af-ford.
pow'r When Thou art nigh.   I need Thee, O I need Thee, Ev-'ry hour I
bide, Or life is vain.
deed, Thou bless-ed Son!

need Thee! O bless me now, my Sav-ior— I come to Thee!

100 Faith Is the Victory

JOHN H. YATES

IRA D. SANKEY

1. En-camped a-long the hills of light, Ye Chris-tian sol-diers, rise,
2. His ban-ner o-ver us is love, Our sword the Word of God;
3. On ev-'ry hand the foe we find Drawn up in dread ar-ray;
4. To him that o-ver-comes the foe White rai-ment shall be giv'n;

And press the bat-tle ere the night Shall veil the glow-ing skies.
We tread the road the saints a-bove With shouts of tri-umph trod.
Let tents of ease be left be-hind, And on-ward to the fray!
Be-fore the an-gels he shall know His name con-fessed in heav'n.

A-gainst the foe in vales be-low Let all our strength be hurled;
By faith they like a whirl-wind's breath Swept on o'er ev-'ry field;
Sal-va-tion's hel-met on each head, With truth all girt a-bout:
Then on-ward from the hills of light, Our hearts with love a-flame;

Faith is the vic-to-ry, we know That o-ver-comes the world.
The faith by which they con-quered death Is still our shin-ing shield.
The earth shall trem-ble 'neath our tread And ech-o with our shout.
We'll van-quish all the hosts of night In Je-sus' con-q'ring name.

CHORUS

Faith is the vic-to-ry! Faith is the vic-to-ry!
Faith is the vic-to-ry! Faith is the vic-to-ry!

O glo-ri-ous vic-to-ry That o-ver-comes the world.

More About Jesus

101

ELIZA E. HEWITT

JOHN R. SWENEY

1. More a-bout Je-sus would I know, More of His grace to oth-ers show,
2. More a-bout Je-sus let me learn, More of His ho-ly will dis-cern;
3. More a-bout Je-sus in His Word Hold-ing com-mun-ion with my Lord,
4. More a-bout Je-sus on His throne, Rich-es in glo-ry all His own,

More of His sav-ing full-ness see, More of His love who died for me.
Spir-it of God, my teach-er be, Show-ing the things of Christ to me.
Hear-ing His voice in ev-'ry line, Mak-ing each faith-ful say-ing mine.
More of His king-dom's sure in-crease, More of His com-ing—Prince of Peace.

REFRAIN

More, more a-bout Je-sus, More, more a-bout Je-sus;

More of His sav-ing full-ness see, More of His love who died for me.

102 Near the Cross

FANNY J. CROSBY

WILLIAM H. DOANE

1. Je - sus, keep me near the cross— There a pre - cious foun - tain,
2. Near the cross, a trem-bling soul, Love and mer - cy found me;
3. Near the cross! O Lamb of God, Bring its scenes be - fore me;
4. Near the cross I'll watch and wait, Hop - ing, trust - ing ev - er,

Free to all, a heal - ing stream, Flows from Cal - v'ry's moun - tain.
There the Bright and Morn-ing Star Sheds its beams a - round me.
Help me walk from day to day With its shad - ows o'er me.
Till I reach the gold - en strand Just be - yond the riv - er.

D.S.— Till my rap-tured soul shall find Rest, be - yond the riv - er.

CHORUS

D.S.

In the cross, in the cross Be my glo - ry ev - er,

103 My Jesus, I Love Thee

WILLIAM R. FEATHERSTON

ADONIRAM J. GORDON

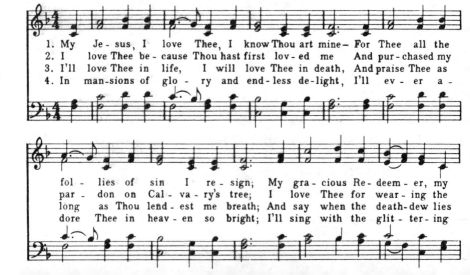

1. My Je - sus, I love Thee, I know Thou art mine— For Thee all the
2. I love Thee be - cause Thou hast first lov - ed me And pur - chased my
3. I'll love Thee in life, I will love Thee in death, And praise Thee as
4. In man - sions of glo - ry and end - less de - light, I'll ev - er a -

fol - lies of sin I re - sign; My gra - cious Re - deem - er, my
par - don on Cal - va - ry's tree; I love Thee for wear - ing the
long as Thou lend - est me breath; And say when the death-dew lies
dore Thee in heav - en so bright; I'll sing with the glit - ter - ing

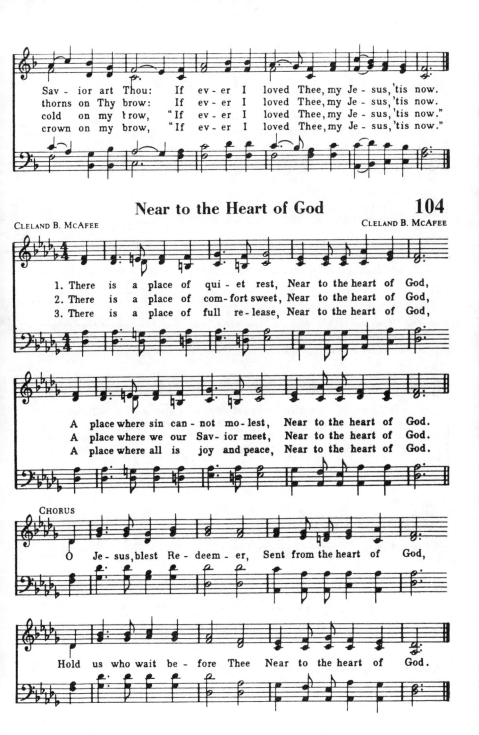

Sav - ior art Thou: If ev - er I loved Thee, my Je - sus, 'tis now.
thorns on Thy brow: If ev - er I loved Thee, my Je - sus, 'tis now.
cold on my brow, "If ev - er I loved Thee, my Je - sus, 'tis now."
crown on my brow, "If ev - er I loved Thee, my Je - sus, 'tis now."

Near to the Heart of God 104

CLELAND B. MCAFEE

CLELAND B. MCAFEE

1. There is a place of qui - et rest, Near to the heart of God,
2. There is a place of com - fort sweet, Near to the heart of God,
3. There is a place of full re - lease, Near to the heart of God,

A place where sin can - not mo - lest, Near to the heart of God.
A place where we our Sav - ior meet, Near to the heart of God.
A place where all is joy and peace, Near to the heart of God.

CHORUS

O Je - sus, blest Re - deem - er, Sent from the heart of God,

Hold us who wait be - fore Thee Near to the heart of God.

105 Sweet Hour of Prayer

William W. Walford

William B. Bradbury

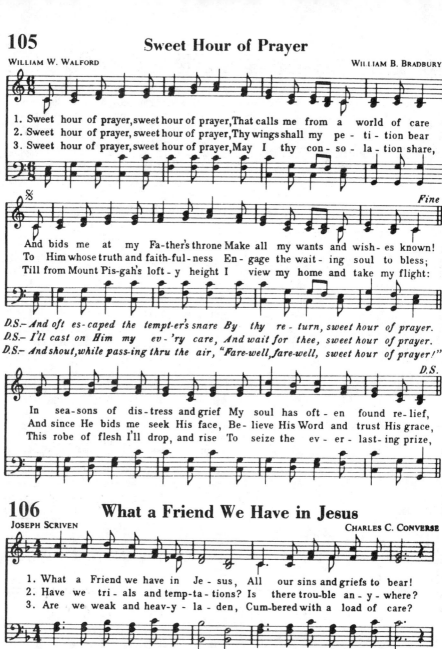

1. Sweet hour of prayer, sweet hour of prayer, That calls me from a world of care
2. Sweet hour of prayer, sweet hour of prayer, Thy wings shall my pe-ti-tion bear
3. Sweet hour of prayer, sweet hour of prayer, May I thy con-so-la-tion share,

Fine

And bids me at my Fa-ther's throne Make all my wants and wish-es known!
To Him whose truth and faith-ful-ness En-gage the wait-ing soul to bless;
Till from Mount Pis-gah's loft-y height I view my home and take my flight:

D.S.– And oft es-caped the tempt-er's snare By thy re-turn, sweet hour of prayer.
D.S.– I'll cast on Him my ev-'ry care, And wait for thee, sweet hour of prayer.
D.S.– And shout, while pass-ing thru the air, "Fare-well, fare-well, sweet hour of prayer!"

D.S.

In sea-sons of dis-tress and grief My soul has oft-en found re-lief,
And since He bids me seek His face, Be-lieve His Word and trust His grace,
This robe of flesh I'll drop, and rise To seize the ev-er-last-ing prize,

106 What a Friend We Have in Jesus

Joseph Scriven

Charles C. Converse

1. What a Friend we have in Je-sus, All our sins and griefs to bear!
2. Have we tri-als and temp-ta-tions? Is there trou-ble an-y-where?
3. Are we weak and heav-y-la-den, Cum-bered with a load of care?

What a priv-i-lege to car-ry Ev-'ry-thing to God in prayer!
We should nev-er be dis-cour-aged—Take it to the Lord in prayer.
Pre-cious Sav-ior, still our ref-uge— Take it to the Lord in prayer.

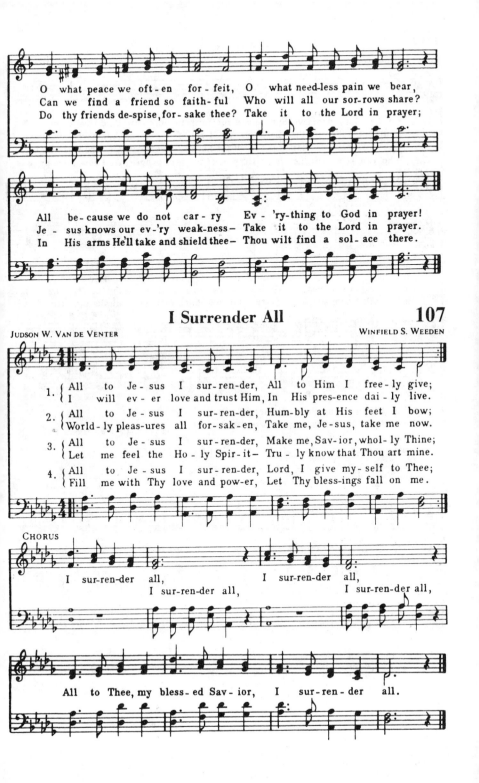

O what peace we oft-en for-feit, O what need-less pain we bear,
Can we find a friend so faith-ful Who will all our sor-rows share?
Do thy friends de-spise, for-sake thee? Take it to the Lord in prayer;

All be-cause we do not car-ry Ev-'ry-thing to God in prayer!
Je - sus knows our ev-'ry weak-ness— Take it to the Lord in prayer.
In His arms He'll take and shield thee— Thou wilt find a sol-ace there.

I Surrender All

107

JUDSON W. VAN DE VENTER

WINFIELD S. WEEDEN

1. { All to Je-sus I sur-ren-der, All to Him I free-ly give;
     I will ev-er love and trust Him, In His pres-ence dai-ly live.

2. { All to Je-sus I sur-ren-der, Hum-bly at His feet I bow;
     World-ly pleas-ures all for-sak-en, Take me, Je-sus, take me now.

3. { All to Je-sus I sur-ren-der, Make me, Sav-ior, whol-ly Thine;
     Let me feel the Ho-ly Spir-it— Tru-ly know that Thou art mine.

4. { All to Je-sus I sur-ren-der, Lord, I give my-self to Thee;
     Fill me with Thy love and pow-er, Let Thy bless-ings fall on me.

CHORUS

I sur-ren-der all, I sur-ren-der all,
I sur-ren-der all, I sur-ren-der all,

All to Thee, my bless-ed Sav-ior, I sur-ren-der all.

108 Is Your All on the Altar?

ELISHA A. HOFFMAN   ELISHA A. HOFFMAN.

1. You have longed for sweet peace and for faith to in-crease, And have earn-est-ly,
2. Would you walk with the Lord in the light of His Word, And have peace and con-
3. O we nev-er can know what the Lord will be-stow Of the bless-ings for
4. Who can tell all the love He will send from a-bove, And how hap-py our

fer-vent-ly prayed; But you can-not have rest or be per-fect-ly blest
tent-ment al-way? You must do His sweet will to be free from all ill-
which we have prayed, Till our bod-y and soul He doth ful-ly con-trol,
hearts will be made, Of the fel-low-ship sweet we shall share at His feet

CHORUS

Un-til all on the al-tar is laid.
On the al-tar your all you must lay.
And our all on the al-tar is laid.
When our all on the al-tar is laid!

Is your all on the al-tar of

sac-ri-fice laid? Your heart does the Spir-it con-trol? You can on-ly be

blest and have peace and sweet rest As you yield Him your bod-y and soul.

Onward, Christian Soldiers

109

SABINE BARING-GOULD   ARTHUR S. SULLIVAN

1. On-ward, Chris-tian sol - diers, March-ing as to war, With the cross of
2. At the sign of tri - umph Sa - tan's host doth flee; On, then, Chris-tian
3. Like a might-y ar - my Moves the Church of God; Broth-ers, we are
4. On-ward, then, ye peo - ple, Join our hap-py throng; Blend with ours your

Je - sus Go - ing on be - fore! Christ, the roy-al Mas - ter, Leads a-
sol - diers, On to vic - to - ry! Hell's foun-da-tions quiv - er At the
tread - ing Where the saints have trod. We are not di - vid - ed, All one
voic - es In the tri - umph song. Glo - ry, laud and hon - or Un - to

gainst the foe; For-ward in - to bat - tle See His ban-ner go!
shout of praise; Broth-ers, lift your voic - es, Loud your an-thems raise!
bod - y we— One in hope and doc - trine, One in char - i - ty.
Christ the King— This thru count-less a - ges Men and an-gels sing.

REFRAIN

On-ward, Chris-tian sol - diers, March-ing as to war,

With the cross of Je - sus Go - ing on be - fore!

110 I Have Decided to Follow Jesus

Attributed to an Indian prince
As sung in Garo, Assam

Folk melody from India
Arr. by Norman Johnson

1. I have de - cid - ed to fol - low Je - sus, I have de - cid - ed
2. Tho no one join me, still I will fol - low, Tho no one join me,
3. The world be-hind me, the cross be-fore me, The world be-hind me,

to fol - low Je - sus, I have de - cid - ed to fol - low Je - sus
still I will fol - low, Tho no one join me, still I will fol - low
the cross be-fore me, The world be-hind me, the cross be-fore me —

No turn-ing back, (No turn-ing back,) no turn-ing back!

111 For God So Loved the World

FRANCES TOWNSEND

ALFRED B. SMITH

1

For God so loved the world He gave His on-ly Son To die on Cal-v'ry's
Some day He's com-ing back—What glo - ry that will

tree, From sin to set me free; be! Won-der-ful His love to me.

Have Thine Own Way, Lord! 112

ADELAIDE A. POLLARD

GEORGE C. STEBBINS

1. Have Thine own way, Lord! Have Thine own way! Thou art the
2. Have Thine own way, Lord! Have Thine own way! Search me and
3. Have Thine own way, Lord! Have Thine own way! Wound-ed and
4. Have Thine own way, Lord! Have Thine own way! Hold o'er my

Pot - ter, I am the clay: Mould me and make me
try me, Mas-ter, to - day! Whit - er than snow, Lord,
wea - ry, Help me, I pray! Pow - er, all pow - er,
be - ing Ab - so - lute sway! Fill with Thy Spir - it

Aft - er Thy will, While I am wait-ing, Yield-ed and still.
Wash me just now, As in Thy pres-ence Hum-bly I bow.
Sure - ly is Thine! Touch me and heal me, Sav-ior di - vine!
Till all shall see Christ on-ly, al-ways, Liv-ing in me!

113   Battle Hymn of the Republic

JULIA WARD HOWE

American melody

1. Mine eyes have seen the glo-ry of the com-ing of the Lord, He is
2. I have seen Him in the watch-fires of a hun-dred cir-cling camps, They have
3. He has sound-ed forth the trum-pet that shall nev-er sound re-treat, He is
4. In the beau-ty of the lil-ies Christ was born a-cross the sea, With a

tram-pling out the vin-tage where the grapes of wrath are stored; He hath loosed the
build-ed Him an al-tar in the eve-ning dews and damps; I can read His
sift-ing out the hearts of men be-fore His judg-ment seat; O be swift, my
glo-ry in His bos-om that trans-fig-ures you and me; As He died to

fate-ful light-ning of His ter-ri-ble swift sword—His truth is march-ing on.
right-eous sen-tence by the dim and flar-ing lamps—His day is march-ing on.
soul, to an-swer Him! be ju-bi-lant, my feet!— Our God is march-ing on.
make men ho-ly, let us die to make men free, While God is march-ing on.

REFRAIN

Glo-ry! glo-ry, hal-le-lu-jah! Glo-ry! glo-ry, hal-le-lu-jah!

Glo-ry! glo-ry, hal-le-lu-jah! His truth is march-ing on.

Happiness Is the Lord

114

Ira F. Stanphill

Ira F. Stanphill

1. Hap - pi - ness is to know the Sav - ior, Liv - ing a life with -
2. Hap - pi - ness is a new cre - a - tion, "Je - sus and me" in
3. Hap - pi - ness is to be for - giv - en, Liv - ing a life that's

in His fa - vor, Hav - ing a change in my be - hav - ior—
close re - la - tion, Hav - ing a part in His sal - va - tion—
worth the liv - in', Tak - ing a trip that leads to heav - en—

Hap - pi - ness is the Lord;
Hap - pi - ness is the Lord. Real joy is mine, no
Hap - pi - ness is the

mat - ter if tear-drops start; I've found the se - cret— it's Je - sus in my heart!

Lord, Hap - pi - ness is the Lord, Hap - pi - ness is the Lord!

115 I Am Thine, O Lord

FANNY J. CROSBY

WILLIAM H. DOANE

1. I am Thine, O Lord— I have heard Thy voice, And it told Thy
2. Con-se-crate me now to Thy serv-ice, Lord, By the pow'r of
3. O the pure de-light of a sin-gle hour That be-fore Thy
4. There are depths of love that I can-not know Till I cross the

love to me; But I long to rise in the arms of faith
grace di-vine; Let my soul look up with a stead-fast hope
throne I spend, When I kneel in pray'r and with Thee, my God,
nar-row sea; There are heights of joy that I may not reach

CHORUS

And be clos-er drawn to Thee.
And my will be lost in Thine. Draw me near - er, near-er,
I com-mune as friend with friend. near-er, near-er,
Till I rest in peace with Thee.

bless-ed Lord, To the cross where Thou hast died; Draw me near-er,

near - er, near-er, bless-ed Lord, To Thy pre-cious, bleed-ing side.

Wonderful Words of Life

116

PHILIP P. BLISS

PHILIP P. BLISS

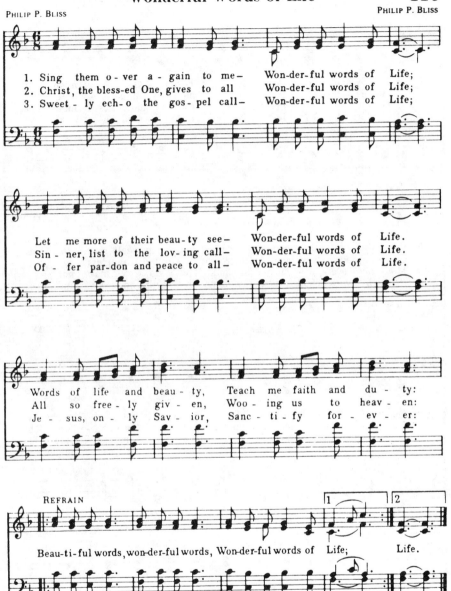

1. Sing them o-ver a-gain to me— Won-der-ful words of Life;
2. Christ, the bless-ed One, gives to all Won-der-ful words of Life;
3. Sweet-ly ech-o the gos-pel call— Won-der-ful words of Life;

Let me more of their beau-ty see— Won-der-ful words of Life.
Sin-ner, list to the lov-ing call— Won-der-ful words of Life.
Of-fer par-don and peace to all— Won-der-ful words of Life.

Words of life and beau-ty, Teach me faith and du-ty:
All so free-ly giv-en, Woo-ing us to heav-en:
Je-sus, on-ly Sav-ior, Sanc-ti-fy for ev-er:

REFRAIN

Beau-ti-ful words, won-der-ful words, Won-der-ful words of Life; Life.

117 Holy, Holy, Holy! Lord God Almighty

1. Ho - ly, ho - ly, ho - ly! Lord God Al - might - y!
2. Ho - ly, ho - ly, ho - ly! all the saints a - dore Thee,
3. Ho - ly, ho - ly, ho - ly! tho' the dark - ness hide Thee,
4. Ho - ly, ho - ly, ho - ly! Lord God Al - might - y!

Ear - ly in the morn - ing our song shall rise to Thee.
Cast - ing down their gold - en crowns a - round the glass - y sea;
Tho' the eye of sin - ful man Thy glo - ry may not see;
All Thy works shall praise Thy name in earth, and sky, and sea.

Ho - ly, ho - ly, ho - ly! mer - ci - ful and might - y!
Cher - u - bim and ser - a - phim fall - ing down be - fore Thee,
On - ly Thou art ho - ly– there is none be - side Thee
Ho - ly, ho - ly, ho - ly! mer - ci - ful and might - y!

God in three Per - sons, bless - ed Trin - i - ty!
Which wert, and art, and ev - er - more shalt be.
Per - fect in pow'r, in love, in pu - ri - ty.
God in three Per - sons, bless - ed Trin - i - ty!

WORDS: Reginald Heber, 1826
MUSIC: John B. Dykes, 1861

Come, Thou Almighty King   118

1. Come, Thou Al - might - y King, Help us Thy
2. Come, Thou In - car - nate Word, Gird on Thy
3. Come, Ho - ly Com - fort - er, Thy sa - cred
4. To Thee, great One in Three, E - ter - nal

name to sing. Help us to praise. Fa - ther all -
might - y sword. Our prayer at - tend. Come, and Thy
wit - ness bear In this glad hour. Thou, who al -
prais - es be Hence ev - er - more. Thy sov - 'reign

glo - ri - ous, O'er all vic - to - ri - ous,
peo - ple bless, And give Thy word suc - cess.
might - y art, Now rule in ev - 'ry heart
maj - es - ty May we in glo - ry see,

Come, and reign o - ver us, An - cient of Days.
Spir - it of ho - li - ness, On us de - scend.
And ne'er from us de - part, Spir - it of pow'r.
And to e - ter - ni - ty Love and a - dore.

WORDS: Anonymous, ca. 1757
MUSIC: Felice de Giardini, 1769

Joyful, Joyful, We Adore Thee

1. Joy - ful, joy - ful, we a - dore Thee, God of glo - ry, Lord of love;
2. All Thy works with joy sur - round Thee; Earth and heav'n re - flect Thy rays.
3. Thou art giv - ing and for - giv - ing, Ev - er bless - ing, ev - er blest.
4. Mor - tals join the might - y cho - rus Which the morn - ing stars be - gan.

Hearts un - fold like flow'rs be - fore Thee, Open - ing to the sun a - bove.
Stars and an - gels sing a - round Thee, Cen - ter of un - bro - ken praise.
Well - spring of the joy of liv - ing, O - cean depth of hap - py rest!
Fa - ther - love is reign - ing o'er us; Broth - er - love binds man to man.

Melt the clouds of sin and sad - ness; Drive the dark of doubt a - way.
Field and for - est, vale and moun - tain, Flow - ery mead - ow, flash - ing sea,
Thou our Fa - ther, Christ our Broth - er— All who live in love are Thine.
Ev - er sing - ing, march we on - ward, Vic - tors in the midst of strife.

Giv - er of im - mor - tal glad - ness, Fill us with the light of day!
Chant - ing bird and flow - ing foun - tain Call us to re - joice in Thee!
Teach us how to love each oth - er; Lift us to the joy di - vine!
Joy - ful mu - sic leads us sun - ward In the tri - umph song of life!

WORDS: Henry van Dyke, 1907
MUSIC: Ludwig van Beethoven, 1824; arr. by Edward Hodges, 1864

WORDS: Joachim Neander, 1680; tr. by Catherine Winkworth, 1863
MUSIC: *Stralsund Gesangbuch*, 1665; harm. by W. Sterndale Bennett, 1864

121   How Great Thou Art

1. O Lord, my God, when I in awe-some won-der Con-sid-er
2. When thro' the woods and for-est glades I wan-der And hear the
3. And when I think that God, His Son not spar-ing, Sent Him to
4. When Christ shall come with shout of ac-cla-ma-tion And take me

all the *worlds Thy hands have made, I see the stars, I hear the
birds sing sweet-ly in the trees, When I look down from loft-y
die, I scarce can take it in; That on the cross, my bur-den
home, what joys shall fill my heart! Then I shall bow in hum-ble

*roll-ing thun-der, Thy pow'r thro'-out the u-ni-verse dis-played.
moun-tain gran-deur And hear the brook and feel the gen-tle breeze,
glad-ly bear-ing, He bled and died to take a-way my sin.
ad-o-ra-tion And there pro-claim: my God, how great Thou art!

Refrain

Then sings my soul, my Sav-ior God, to Thee. How great Thou

*Author's original words are "works" and "mighty".

WORDS and MUSIC: Stuart K. Hine, 1953

art! How great Thou art! Then sings my soul, my Sav - ior

God, to Thee. How great Thou art! How great Thou art!

Sanctuary

122

Lord, pre - pare me to be a sanc - tu - ar - y, pure and

ho - ly, tried and true; With thanks- giv - ing, I'll be a

liv - ing sanc-tu-ar - y for You.

Words and Music by John Thompson and Randy Scruggs

123 Immortal, Invisible, God Only Wise

1. Im - mor - tal, in - vis - i - ble, God on - ly wise,
2. Un - rest - ing, un - hast - ing, and si - lent as light,
3. To all, life Thou giv - est— to both great and small;
4. Great Fa - ther of glo - ry, pure Fa - ther of light,

In light in - ac - ces - si - ble hid from our eyes,
Nor want - ing, nor wast - ing, Thou rul - est in might;
In all life Thou liv - est— the true Life of all.
Thine an - gels a - dore Thee, all veil - ing their sight.

Most bless - ed, most glo - rious, the An - cient of Days,
Thy jus - tice, like moun - tains, high soar - ing a - bove
Thy wis - dom so bound - less, Thy mer - cy so free,
All laud we would ren - der— O help us to see

Al - might - y, vic - to - rious— Thy great name we praise.
Thy clouds, which are foun - tains of good - ness and love.
E - ter - nal Thy good - ness, for naught chang - eth Thee.
'Tis on - ly the splen - dor of light hid - eth Thee.

WORDS: Walter Chalmers Smith, 1867
MUSIC: Welsh Hymn Tune, 1839; harm. by John Roberts, 1839

All Hail King Jesus

124

All hail King Je - sus. All hail Em - man - u - el,

King of Kings, Lord of Lords, Bright Morn - ing Star.

And thro' - out e - ter - ni - ty, I'll sing His prais - es,

And I'll reign with Him thro' - out e - ter - ni - ty.

125 Grace Greater than Our Sin

1. Mar - vel - ous grace of our lov - ing Lord, Grace that ex - ceeds our
2. Dark is the stain that we can - not hide, What can a - vail to
3. Mar - vel - ous, in - fi - nite, match - less grace, Free - ly be - stowed on

sin and our guilt, Yon - der on Cal - va - ry's mount out - poured,
wash it a - way? Look! there is flow - ing a crim - son tide;
all who be - lieve; All who are long - ing to see His face,

There where the blood of the Lamb was spilt. Grace, grace,
Whit - er than snow you may be to - day. Mar - vel - ous grace,
Will you this mo - ment His grace re - ceive?

God's grace, Grace that will par - don and cleanse with - in; Grace,
in - fi - nite grace, Mar - vel - ous

grace, God's grace, Grace that is great-er than all our sin.
grace, in-fi-nite grace,

God of Our Fathers 126

DANIEL C. ROBERTS

GEORGE W. WARREN

Trumpets,
before each verse

1. God of our fa-thers, whose al-might-y hand
2. Thy love di-vine hath led us in the past,
3. From war's a-larms, from dead-ly pes-ti-lence,
4. Re-fresh Thy peo-ple on their toil-some way,

Leads forth in beau-ty all the star-ry band Of shin-ing worlds in
In this free land by Thee our lot is cast; Be Thou our rul - er,
Be Thy strong arm our ev-er-sure de-fense; Thy true re-li - gion
Lead us from night to nev-er-end-ing day; Fill all our lives with

splen-dor thru the skies, Our grate-ful songs be-fore Thy throne a-rise.
guard-ian, guide, and stay, Thy word our law, Thy paths our cho-sen way.
in our hearts in-crease, Thy boun-teous good-ness nour-ish us in peace.
love and grace di-vine, And glo-ry, laud, and praise be ev-er Thine!

127 # He Leadeth Me

1. He lead-eth me! O bless-ed tho't! O words with
2. Some-times 'mid scenes of deep-est gloom, Some-times where
3. Lord, I would clasp Thy hand in mine, Nor ev-er
4. And when my task on earth is done, When by Thy

heav'n-ly com-fort fraught! What-e'er I do, wher-e'er I be,
E - den's bow-ers bloom, By wa - ters still, o'er trou-bled sea,
mur - mur nor re - pine, Con - tent, what-ev - er lot I see,
grace the vic-t'ry's won, E'en death's cold wave I will not flee,

Refrain

Still 'tis God's hand that lead-eth me.
Still 'tis His hand that lead-eth me. He lead-eth me; He
Since 'tis my God that lead-eth me.
Since God thro' Jor - dan lead-eth me.

lead-eth me. By His own hand He lead-eth me. His

WORDS: Joseph H. Gilmore, 1862
MUSIC: William B. Bradbury, 1864

faith-ful fol-l'wer I would be, For by His hand He lead-eth me.

Stand Up for Jesus 128

GEORGE DUFFIELD

GEORGE J. WEBB

1. Stand up, stand up for Je - sus, Ye sol - diers of the cross!
2. Stand up, stand up for Je - sus, The trum - pet call o - bey;
3. Stand up, stand up for Je - sus, Stand in His strength a - lone;
4. Stand up, stand up for Je - sus, The strife will not be long;

Lift high His roy - al ban - ner— It must not suf - fer loss.
Forth to the might - y con - flict In this His glo - rious day.
The arm of flesh will fail you— Ye dare not trust your own.
This day the noise of bat - tle— The next, the vic - tor's song.

From vic - t'ry un - to vic - t'ry His ar - my shall He lead,
Ye that are men now serve Him A - gainst un - num - bered foes;
Put on the gos - pel ar - mor, Each piece put on with prayer;
To Him that o - ver - com - eth A crown of life shall be:

Till ev - 'ry foe is van - quished And Christ is Lord in - deed.
Let cour - age rise with dan - ger And strength to strength op - pose.
Where du - ty calls or dan - ger, Be nev - er want - ing there.
He with the King of glo - ry Shall reign e - ter - nal - ly.

129 **Majesty**

Maj - es - ty, wor - ship His maj - es - ty. Un - to

Je - sus be all glo - ry, hon - or, and praise. Maj - es - ty,

king - dom au - thor - i - ty Flow from His throne un - to His own;

WORDS: Jack Hayford, 1981
MUSIC: Jack Hayford, 1981; arr. by Eugene Thomas, 1986

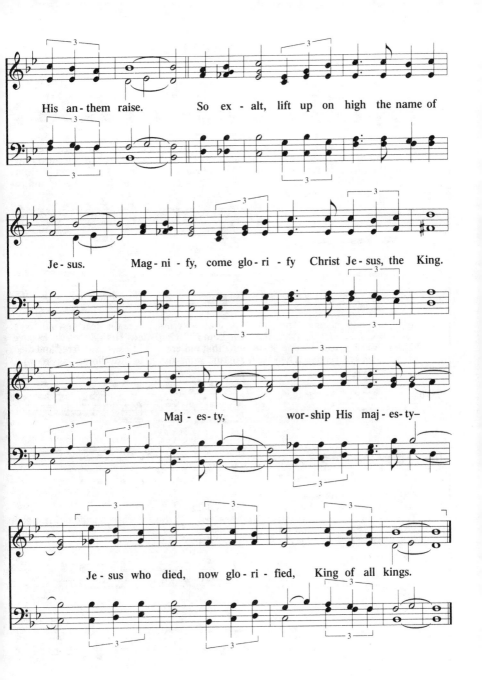

His an-them raise. So ex - alt, lift up on high the name of

Je - sus. Mag - ni - fy, come glo - ri - fy Christ Je - sus, the King.

Maj - es - ty, wor-ship His maj - es- ty–

Je - sus who died, now glo - ri - fied, King of all kings.

The Old Rugged Cross

1. On a hill far a-way stood an old rug-ged cross, The em-blem of
2. O the old rug-ged cross, so de-spised by the world, Has a won-drous at-
3. In the old rug-ged cross, stained with blood so di-vine, A won-drous
4. To the old rug-ged cross I will ev-er be true, Its shame and re-

suf-f'ring and shame; And I love that old cross, where the dear-est and best
trac-tion for me; For the dear Lamb of God left His glo-ry a-bove
beau-ty I see; For 'twas on that old cross Je-sus suf-fered and died
proach glad-ly bear. Then He'll call me some-day to my home far a-way,

For a world of lost sin-ners was slain.
To bear it to dark Cal-va-ry.
To par-don and sanc-ti-fy me.
Where His glo-ry for-ev-er I'll share.

Refrain

So I'll cher-ish the old rug-ged cross, the

cross,_____ Till my tro-phies at last I lay down. I will cling to the
old rug-ged cross,

WORDS and MUSIC: George Bennard, 1913

old rug-ged cross,_____ And ex-change it some-day for a crown.
cross, the old rug-ged cross,

More Precious than Silver 131

Lord, You are more pre-cious than sil-ver; Lord, You are more

cost-ly than gold. Lord, You are more beau-ti-ful than

dia-monds, And noth-ing I de-sire com-pares with You.

TEXT: Lynn De Shazo
MUSIC: Lynn De Shazo

132 There Is a Redeemer

1. There is a Re - deem - er– Je - sus, God's own Son,
2. Je - sus, my Re - deem - er, name a - bove all names,
3. When I stand in Glo - ry, I will see His face;

Pre - cious Lamb of God, Mes - si - ah, Ho - ly One.
Pre - cious Lamb of God, Mes - si - ah, O for sin - ners slain.
There I'll serve my King for - ev - er in that ho - ly place.

Refrain

Thank You, O my Fa - ther, for giv - ing us Your Son, And

leav - ing Your Spir - it till the work on earth is done.

Crown Him with Many Crowns

1. Crown Him with man - y crowns, The Lamb up - on His throne.
2. Crown Him the Lord of Love! Be - hold His hands and side–
3. Crown Him the Lord of Life! Who tri - umphed o'er the grave;
4. Crown Him the Lord of Heav'n! One with the Fa - ther known,

Hark! how the heav'n-ly an - them drowns All mu - sic but its own!
Rich wounds, yet vis - i - ble a - bove, In beau - ty glo - ri - fied.
Who rose vic - to - rious to the strife For those He came to save.
One with the Spir - it thro' Him giv'n From yon - der glo - rious throne.

A - wake, my soul, and sing Of Him who died for thee, And
No an - gel in the sky Can ful - ly bear that sight, But
His glo - ries now we sing Who died and rose on high, Who
To Thee be end - less praise, For Thou for us hast died. Be

hail Him as thy match - less King Thro' all e - ter - ni - ty.
down - ward bends his won - d'ring eyes At mys - ter - ies so bright.
died e - ter - nal life to bring, And lives that death may die.
Thou, O Lord, thro' end - less days A - dored and mag - ni - fied!

WORDS: Stanzas 1, 2, 4, Matthew Bridges, 1854; stanza 3, Godfrey Thring, 1874
MUSIC: George J. Elvey, 1868

134 Because He Lives

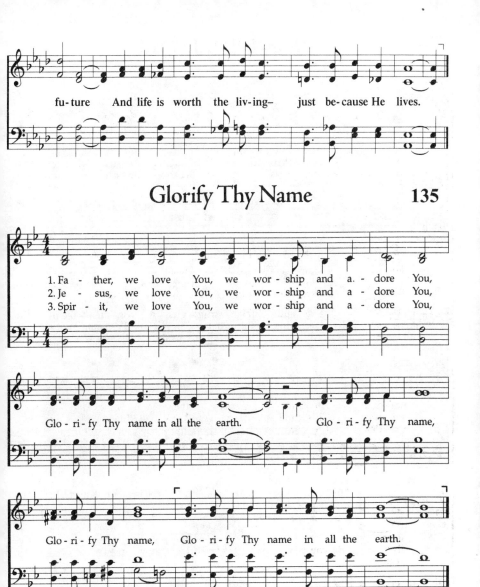

fu - ture And life is worth the liv-ing– just be-cause He lives.

Glorify Thy Name

135

1. Fa - ther, we love You, we wor - ship and a - dore You,
2. Je - sus, we love You, we wor - ship and a - dore You,
3. Spir - it, we love You, we wor - ship and a - dore You,

Glo - ri - fy Thy name in all the earth. Glo - ri - fy Thy name,

Glo - ri - fy Thy name, Glo - ri - fy Thy name in all the earth.

TEXT: Donna Adkins
MUSIC: Donna Adkins

Jesus Is Lord of All

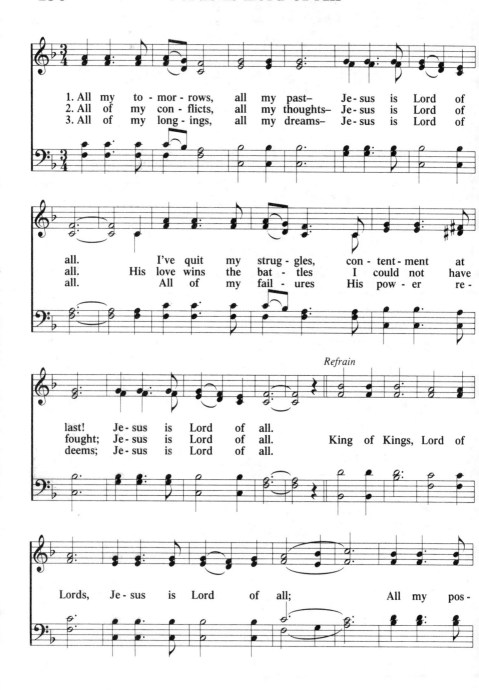

1. All my to-mor-rows, all my past— Je-sus is Lord of
2. All of my con-flicts, all my thoughts— Je-sus is Lord of
3. All of my long-ings, all my dreams— Je-sus is Lord of

all.   I've quit my strug-gles, con-tent-ment at
all.   His love wins the bat-tles I could not have
all.   All of my fail-ures His pow-er re-

Refrain

last!   Je-sus is Lord of all.
fought; Je-sus is Lord of all.   King of Kings, Lord of
deems; Je-sus is Lord of all.

Lords, Je-sus is Lord of all;   All my pos-

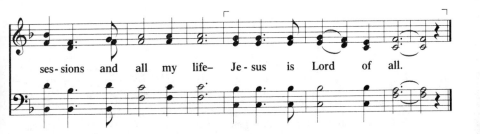

ses - sions and all my life– Je - sus is Lord of all.

Rejoice, the Lord Is King 137

1. Re - joice, the Lord is King; Your Lord and King a - dore!
2. Je - sus, the Sav - ior, reigns, The God of truth and love.
3. His king - dom can - not fail; He rules o'er earth and heav'n.
4. Re - joice in glo - rious hope! Our Lord, the Judge, shall come

Re - joice, give thanks, and sing, And tri - umph ev - er - more. Lift
When He had purged our stains, He took His seat a - bove. Lift
The keys of death and hell Are to our Je - sus giv'n. Lift
And take His ser - vants up To their e - ter - nal home. Lift

up your heart; Lift up your voice! Re - joice; a - gain I say: re - joice!
up your heart; Lift up your voice! Re - joice; a - gain I say: re - joice!
up your heart; Lift up your voice! Re - joice; a - gain I say: re - joice!
up your heart; Lift up your voice! Re - joice; a - gain I say: re - joice!

WORDS: Charles Wesley, 1746
MUSIC: John Darwall, 1770

138 Spirit Song

1. O let the Son of God en-fold you with His Spir-it
2. O come and sing the song with glad-ness as your hearts are

and His love; Let Him fill your heart and sat-is-fy your soul.
filled with joy; Lift your hands in sweet sur-ren-der to His name.

O let Him have the things that hold you, and His Spir-it, like a
O give Him all your tears and sad-ness; give Him all your years of

dove, Will de-scend up-on your life and make you whole.
pain, And you'll en-ter in-to life in Je-sus' name.

Refrain

Je-sus, O Je-sus, come and fill Your lambs.

WORDS and MUSIC: John Wimber, 1979

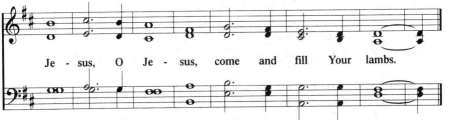

Je - sus, O Je - sus, come and fill Your lambs.

Praise the Name of Jesus 139

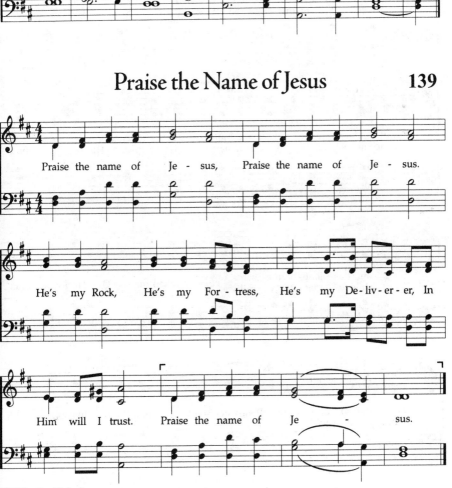

Praise the name of Je - sus, Praise the name of Je - sus.

He's my Rock, He's my For - tress, He's my De - liv - er - er, In

Him will I trust. Praise the name of Je - sus.

TEXT: Roy Hicks, Jr.
MUSIC: Roy Hicks, Jr.

140 He Touched Me

1. Shack - led by a heav-y bur-den, 'Neath a load of guilt and shame— Then the hand of Je-sus touched me, And now I am no long-er the same.

2. Since I met this bless-ed Sav-ior, Since He cleansed and made me whole, I will nev-er cease to praise Him— I'll shout it while e - ter-ni-ty rolls.

Refrain

He touched me, O He touched me, And O the joy that floods my soul! Some-thing hap-pened, and now I know, He touched me and made me whole.

Words and Music by William J. Gaither.
Copyright © 1963 William J. Gaither, Inc. All rights controlled by Gaither Copyright Management.
Used by permission.

Love Lifted Me

141

WORDS: James Rowe, 1912
MUSIC: Howard E. Smith, 1912

142 Victory in Jesus

1. I heard an old, old sto-ry, how a Sav-ior came from glo-ry,
2. I heard a-bout His heal-ing, of His cleans-ing pow'r re-veal-ing,
3. I heard a-bout a man-sion He has built for me in glo-ry,

How He gave His life on Cal-va-ry to save a wretch like me.
How He made the lame to walk a-gain and caused the blind to see.
And I heard a-bout the streets of gold be-yond the crys-tal sea,

I heard a-bout His groan-ing, of His pre-cious blood's a-ton-ing,
And then I cried, "Dear Je-sus, come and heal my bro-ken spir-it";
A-bout the an-gels sing-ing, and the old re-demp-tion sto-ry;

Then I re-pent-ed of my sins and won the vic-to-ry.
And some-how Je-sus came and brought to me the vic-to-ry.
And some sweet day I'll sing up there the song of vic-to-ry.

WORDS and MUSIC: Eugene M. Bartlett, 1939

Refrain

O vic-to-ry in Je-sus, my Sav-ior for-ev-er!

He sought me and bought me with His re-deem-ing blood.

He loved me ere I knew Him, and all my love is due Him.

He plunged me to vic-to-ry be-neath the cleans-ing flood.

143 Wonderful Grace of Jesus

1. Won - der - ful grace of Je - sus, Great - er than all my sin—
2. Won - der - ful grace of Je - sus, Reach - ing to all the lost—
3. Won - der - ful grace of Je - sus, Reach - ing the most de - filed—

How shall my tongue de - scribe it? Where shall His praise be - gin?
By it I have been par - doned, Saved to the ut - ter - most.
By its trans-form - ing pow - er Mak - ing him God's dear child,

Tak - ing a - way my bur - den, Set - ting my spir - it free;
Chains have been torn a - sun - der, Giv - ing me lib - er - ty;
Pur - chas - ing peace and heav - en For all e - ter - ni - ty;

For the won - der - ful grace of Je - sus reach - es me.
For the won - der - ful grace of Je - sus reach - es me.
And the won - der - ful grace of Je - sus reach - es me.

Refrain

Won - der - ful the match - less grace, the match - less grace of Je - sus,
Won - der - ful the match - less grace of Je - sus,

Men unison

WORDS and MUSIC: Haldor Lillenas, 1918

144   I Will Sing the Wondrous Story

1. I will sing the won-drous sto - ry Of the Christ who died for me—
2. I was lost, but Je-sus found me, Found the sheep that went a - stray,
3. I was bruised, but Je-sus healed me; Faint was I from many a fall.
4. Days of dark-ness still come o'er me; Sor-row's paths I of-ten tread.
5. He will keep me till the riv - er Rolls its wa - ters at my feet;

How He left His home in glo - ry For the cross of Cal - va - ry.
Threw His lov - ing arms a - round me, Drew me back in - to His way.
Sight was gone, and fears pos-sessed me, But He freed me from them all.
But the Sav - ior still is with me; By His hand I'm safe-ly led.
Then He'll bear me safe-ly o - ver, Where the loved ones I shall meet.

Refrain

Yes, I'll sing_____ the won-drous sto - ry Of the
Yes, I'll sing   the won-drous sto - ry

Christ_____ who died for me— Sing it with_____ the saints in
Of the Christ   who died for me— Sing it with

WORDS: Francis H. Rowley, 1886
MUSIC: Peter P. Bilhorn, 1886

Blessed Be the Lord God Almighty **145**

TEXT: Bob Fitts
MUSIC: Bob Fitts

The Lily of the Valley

1. I've found a Friend in Je - sus; He's ev - 'ry - thing to me.
2. He all my griefs has tak - en, and all my sor - rows borne.
3. He'll nev - er, nev - er leave me, nor yet for - sake me here,

He's the fair - est of ten thou - sand to my soul. The
In temp - ta - tion He's my strong and might - y Tow'r. I've
While I live by faith and do His bless - ed will. A

Lil - y of the Val - ley, in Him a - lone I see
all for Him for - sak - en; I've all my i - dols torn
wall of fire a - bout me, I've noth - ing now to fear.

All I need to cleanse and make me ful - ly whole.
From my heart, and now He keeps me by His pow'r.
With His man - na He my hun - gry soul shall fill.

WORDS: Charles W. Fry
MUSIC: William S. Hays

In sor-row He's my com-fort; in trou-ble He's my stay. He
Tho' all the world for-sake me, and Sa-tan tempt me sore, Thro'
Then sweep-ing up to glo-ry, I'll see His bless-ed face, Where

tells me ev-'ry care on Him to roll.
Je-sus I shall safe-ly reach the goal.
riv-ers of de-light shall ev-er roll.

He's the Lil-y of the Val-ley,

the Bright and Morn-ing Star. He's the fair-est of ten thou-sand to my soul.

147   The Haven of Rest

1. My soul in sad ex-ile was out on life's sea, So bur-dened with
2. I yield-ed my-self to His ten-der em-brace, And faith tak-ing
3. The song of my soul, since the Lord made me whole, Has been the old
4. O come to the Sav-ior. He pa-tient-ly waits To save by His

sin and dis-tressed, Till I heard a sweet voice say-ing, "Make Me your
hold of the Word, My fet-ters fell off, and I an-chored my
sto-ry so blest, Of Je-sus, who'll save who-so-ev-er will
pow-er di-vine. Come, an-chor your soul in the ha-ven of

D.S. tem-pest may sweep o'er the wild, storm-y

choice," And I en-tered the ha-ven of rest.
soul. The Ha-ven of Rest is my Lord.
have A home in the ha-ven of rest.
rest, And say, "My Be-lov-ed is mine."

Fine ¬ *Refrain*

I've an-chored my soul

deep; In Je-sus I'm safe ev-er-more.

in the ha-ven of rest. I'll sail the wide seas no more. The

D.S. al Fine

WORDS: Henry L. Gilmour, 1890
MUSIC: George D. Moore, 1890

My Faith Has Found a Resting Place

1. My faith has found a rest-ing place– Not in de-vice nor creed:
2. E-nough for me that Je-sus saves– This ends my fear and doubt;
3. My heart is lean-ing on the Word– The writ-ten Word of God;
4. My great Phy-si-cian heals the sick– The lost He came to save:

I trust the Ev-er-liv-ing One– His wounds for me shall plead.
A sin-ful soul, I come to Him– He'll nev-er cast me out.
Sal-va-tion by my Sav-ior's name, Sal-va-tion thro' His blood.
For me His pre-cious blood He shed– For me His life He gave.

Refrain

I need no oth-er ar-gu-ment; I need no oth-er plea.

It is e-nough that Je-sus died, And that He died for me.

WORDS: Lidie H. Edmunds, ca. 1891
MUSIC: Norwegian Folk Melody; arr. by William J. Kirkpatrick, 1891

149 Since Jesus Came into My Heart

1. What a won - der - ful change in my life has been wrought
2. I have ceased from my wan - d'ring and go - ing a - stray
3. I'm pos - sessed of a hope that is stead - fast and sure,
4. There's a light in the val - ley of death now for me,
5. I shall go there to dwell in that cit - y I know,

Since Je - sus came in - to my heart! I have light in my
Since Je - sus came in - to my heart; And my sins which were
Since Je - sus came in - to my heart; And no dark clouds of
Since Je - sus came in - to my heart; And the gates of the
Since Je - sus came in - to my heart; And I'm hap - py, so

soul for which long I had sought, Since Je - sus came in - to my
man - y are all washed a - way, Since Je - sus came in - to my
doubt now my path - way ob - scure, Since Je - sus came in - to my
cit - y be - yond I can see, Since Je - sus came in - to my
hap - py, as on - ward I go, Since Je - sus came in - to my

Refrain

heart.
heart.
heart.
heart.
heart.

Since Je - sus came in - to my heart,   Since
Since Je - sus came in,   came in - to my heart, Since

WORDS: Rufus H. McDaniel, 1914
MUSIC: Charles H. Gabriel, 1914

Je-sus came in-to my heart,
Je-sus came in, came in-to my heart,

Floods of joy o'er my

soul like the sea bil-lows roll, Since Je-sus came in-to my heart.

Father, I Adore You

150

II

1. Fa - ther, I a - dore You, Lay my life be -
2. Je - sus, I a - dore You, Lay my life be -
3. Spir - it, I a - dore You, Lay my life be -

III

fore You; How I love You.
fore You; How I love You.
fore You; How I love You.

TEXT: Terrye Coelho Strom
MUSIC: Terrye Coelho Strom

151

I'd Rather Have Jesus

1. I'd rath - er have Je - sus than sil - ver or gold; I'd
2. I'd rath - er have Je - sus than men's ap - plause; I'd
3. He's fair - er than lil - ies of rar - est bloom; He's

rath - er be His than have rich - es un - told; I'd rath - er
rath - er be faith - ful to His dear cause; I'd rath - er
sweet - er than hon - ey from out the comb; He's all that

have Je - sus than hous - es or lands. I'd rath - er be
have Je - sus than world - wide fame. I'd rath - er be
my hun - ger - ing spir - it needs. I'd rath - er have

cued notes 3rd stanza   *Refrain*

led by His nail - pierced hand
true to His ho - ly name Than to be the king of a
Je - sus and let Him lead

WORDS: Rhea F. Miller, 1922
MUSIC: George Beverly Shea, 1939

vast do-main And be held in sin's dread sway. I'd rath-er have

Je-sus than an-y-thing This world af-fords to-day.

Take My Life and Let It Be 152

FRANCES R. HAVERGAL

H. A. CÉSAR MALAN

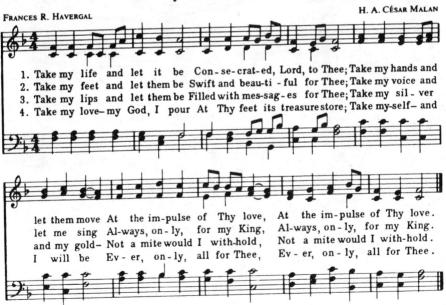

1. Take my life and let it be Con-se-crat-ed, Lord, to Thee; Take my hands and
2. Take my feet and let them be Swift and beau-ti-ful for Thee; Take my voice and
3. Take my lips and let them be Filled with mes-sag-es for Thee; Take my sil-ver
4. Take my love—my God, I pour At Thy feet its treasure store; Take my-self—and

let them move At the im-pulse of Thy love, At the im-pulse of Thy love.
let me sing Al-ways, on-ly, for my King, Al-ways, on-ly, for my King.
and my gold— Not a mite would I with-hold, Not a mite would I with-hold.
I will be Ev-er, on-ly, all for Thee, Ev-er, on-ly, all for Thee.

153 Open My Eyes, That I May See

1. O-pen my eyes, that I may see Glimps-es of truth Thou hast for
2. O-pen my ears, that I may hear Voic-es of truth Thou send-est
3. O-pen my mouth and let me bear Glad-ly the warm truth ev-'ry-
4. O-pen my mind, that I may read More of Thy love in word and

me; Place in my hands the won-der-ful key That shall un-clasp and
clear; And while the wave-notes fall on my ear, Ev-'ry-thing false will
where; O-pen my heart and let me pre-pare Love with Thy chil-dren
deed. What shall I fear while yet Thou dost lead? On-ly for light from

Refrain

set me free.
dis-ap-pear. Si-lent-ly now I wait for Thee, Read-y, my God, Thy
thus to share.
Thee I plead.

will to see. O-pen my eyes; il-lu-mine me, Spir-it di-vine.
ears,
heart,
mind,

WORDS and MUSIC: Clara H. Scott, 1895

In the Garden

1. I come to the gar - den a - lone, While the dew is still on the ros - es; And the voice I hear, Fall - ing on my ear, The Son of God dis - clos - es.

2. He speaks, and the sound of His voice Is so sweet the birds hush their sing - ing, And the mel - o - dy That He gave to me With - in my heart is ring - ing.

3. I'd stay in the gar - den with Him Tho' the night a - round me is fall - ing, But He bids me go; Thro' the voice of woe, His voice to me is call - ing.

Refrain

And He walks with me, and He talks with me, And He tells me I am His own; And the joy we share as we tar - ry there, None oth - er has ev - er known.

WORDS and MUSIC: C. Austin Miles, 1912

155   Make Me a Blessing

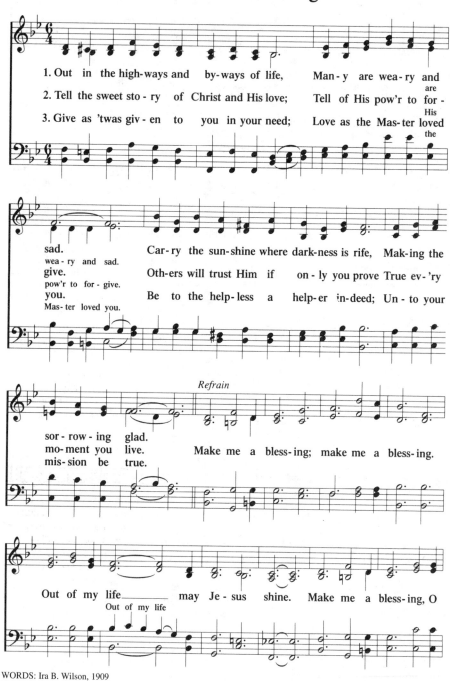

1. Out in the high-ways and by-ways of life, Man-y are wea-ry and
2. Tell the sweet sto-ry of Christ and His love; Tell of His pow'r to for-
3. Give as 'twas giv-en to you in your need; Love as the Mas-ter loved

sad.
wea-ry and sad.
give.
pow'r to for-give.
you.
Mas-ter loved you.

Car-ry the sun-shine where dark-ness is rife, Mak-ing the
Oth-ers will trust Him if on-ly you prove True ev-'ry
Be to the help-less a help-er in-deed; Un-to your

Refrain

sor-row-ing glad.
mo-ment you live.
mis-sion be true.

Make me a bless-ing; make me a bless-ing.

Out of my life_____ may Je-sus shine. Make me a bless-ing, O
Out of my life

WORDS: Ira B. Wilson, 1909
MUSIC: George S. Schuler, 1924

Sav-ior, I pray.————— Make me a bless-ing to some-one to-day.
I pray Thee, my Sav - ior.

Jesus, Lover of My Soul 156

CHARLES WESLEY

SIMEON B. MARSH

Fine

1. { Je - sus, lov - er of my soul, Let me to Thy bos - om fly,
   { While the near - er wa - ters roll, While the tem - pest still is high!

2. { Oth - er ref - uge have I none— Hangs my help-less soul on Thee;
   { Leave, ah, leave me not a - lone, Still sup-port and com-fort me!

3. { Thou, O Christ, art all I want, More than all in Thee I find;
   { Raise the fall - en, cheer the faint, Heal the sick and lead the blind.

4. { Plen-teous grace with Thee is found, Grace to cov - er all my sin;
   { Let the heal-ing streams a-bound, Make and keep me pure with - in.

D.C.— Safe in - to the ha - ven guide, O re - ceive my soul at last!
D.C.— Cov - er my de - fense-less head With the shad- ow of Thy wing.
D.C.— False and full of sin I am, Thou art full of truth and grace.
D.C.— Spring Thou up with - in my heart, Rise to all e - ter - ni - ty.

D.C.

Hide me, O my Sav - ior, hide— Till the storm of life is past;
All my trust on Thee is stayed— All my help from Thee I bring;
Just and ho - ly is Thy name— I am all un - right-eous-ness;
Thou of life the foun-tain art— Free-ly let me take of Thee;

157 Freely, Freely

1. God for-gave my sin in Je-sus' name; I've been born a-gain in
2. All pow'r is giv'n in Je-sus' name, In earth and heav'n in

Je-sus' name; And in Je-sus' name I come to you To share His
Je-sus' name; And in Je-sus' name I come to you To share His

Refrain

love as He told me to. He said, "Free - ly, free - ly
pow'r as He told me to.

you have re-ceived; Free - ly, free - ly give. Go in My

name and, be-cause you be-lieve, Oth-ers will know that I live."

WORDS and MUSIC: Carol Owens, 1972

He Is Exalted

158

159

Count Your Blessings

1. When up-on life's bil-lows you are tem-pest-tossed,
2. Are you ev-er bur-dened with a load of care?
3. When you look at oth-ers with their lands and gold,
4. So a-mid the con-flict, wheth-er great or small,

When you are dis-cour-aged, think-ing all is lost,
Does the cross seem heav-y you are called to bear?
Think that Christ has prom-ised you His wealth un-told.
Do not be dis-cour-aged; God is o-ver all.

Count your man-y bless-ings– name them one by one–
Count your man-y bless-ings; ev-'ry doubt will fly,
Count your man-y bless-ings; mon-ey can-not buy
Count your man-y bless-ings; an-gels will at-tend,

And it will sur-prise you what the Lord hath done.
And you will be sing-ing as the days go by.
Your re-ward in heav-en nor your home on high.
Help and com-fort give you to your jour-ney's end.

WORDS: Johnson Oatman, Jr., 1897
MUSIC: Edwin O. Excell, 1897

160 God, Our Father, We Adore Thee

1. God, our Fa - ther, we a - dore Thee! We, Thy chil - dren, bless Thy name!
2. Son E - ter - nal, we a - dore Thee! Lamb up - on the throne on high!
3. Ho - ly Spir - it, we a - dore Thee! Par - a - clete and heav'n - ly guest!
4. Fa - ther, Son, and Ho - ly Spir - it— Three in One! we give Thee praise!

Cho - sen in the Christ be - fore Thee, We are "ho - ly, with - out blame."
Lamb of God, we bow be - fore Thee, Thou hast bro't Thy peo - ple nigh!
Sent from God and from the Sav - ior, Thou hast led us in - to rest.
For the rich - es we in - her - it, Heart and voice to Thee we raise!

We a - dore Thee! we a - dore Thee! Ab - ba's prais - es we pro - claim!
We a - dore Thee! we a - dore Thee! Son of God, who came to die!
We a - dore Thee! we a - dore Thee! By Thy grace for - ev - er blest;
We a - dore Thee! we a - dore Thee! Thee we bless thro' end - less days!

We a - dore Thee! we a - dore Thee! Ab - ba's prais - es we pro - claim!
We a - dore Thee! we a - dore Thee! Son of God, who came to die!
We a - dore Thee! we a - dore Thee! By Thy grace for - ev - er blest!
We a - dore Thee! we a - dore Thee! Thee we bless thro' end - less days!

TEXT: George W. Frazier; Alfred S. Loizeaux, stanza 3
MUSIC: John Zundel

Thou Art Worthy

Thou art wor-thy, Thou art wor-thy, Thou art wor-thy, O Lord,

To re-ceive glo-ry, glo-ry and hon-or, Glo-ry and

hon-or and pow'r. For Thou hast cre-at-ed, hast all things cre-

at-ed; Thou hast cre-at-ed all things. And for Thy

plea-sure they are cre-at-ed; For Thou art wor-thy, O Lord.

TEXT: Pauline M. Mills; based on Revelations 4:11; 5:9
MUSIC: Pauline M. Mills

162   Lord, I Lift Your Name on High

Lord, I lift Your name on high; Lord, I love to sing Your prais - es. I'm so glad You're in my life; I'm so glad You came to save us. You came from heav-en to earth to show the way; From the earth to the cross, my debt to pay. From the cross to the grave, From the grave to the

COMPOSER: Rick Founds

sky; Lord, I lift Your name on high.

Nothing But the Blood

163

ROBERT LOWRY

ROBERT LOWRY

1. What can wash a-way my sin? Noth-ing but the blood of Je - sus;
2. For my par-don this I see— Noth-ing but the blood of Je - sus;
3. Noth-ing can for sin a-tone— Noth-ing but the blood of Je - sus;
4. This is all my hope and peace— Noth-ing but the blood of Je - sus;

What can make me whole a-gain? Noth-ing but the blood of Je - sus.
For my cleans-ing, this my plea— Noth-ing but the blood of Je - sus.
Naught of good that I have done— Noth-ing but the blood of Je - sus.
This is all my right-eous-ness— Noth-ing but the blood of Je - sus.

REFRAIN

Oh! pre-cious is the flow That makes me white as snow;

No oth-er fount I know, Noth-ing but the blood of Je - sus.

164

His Name Is Wonderful

His name is Won-der-ful, His name is Won-der-ful, His name is Won-der-ful,

Je-sus, my Lord; He is the might-y King, Mas-ter of ev-ery-thing,

His name is Won-der-ful, Je-sus, my Lord. He's the great Shep-herd, the Rock of all

ag-es, Al-might-y God is He; Bow down be-fore Him, Love and a-

dore Him; His name is Won-der-ful, Je-sus, my Lord.

TEXT: Audrey Mieir
MUSIC: Audrey Mieir

Awesome God

165

Our God is an awe-some God; He reigns from heav-en a-bove With wis-dom, pow'r and love; Our God is an awe-some God! Our God! Our God is an awe-some God; He reigns from heav-en a-bove With wis-dom, pow'r and love; Our God is an awe-some God! Our God! Our God is an awe-some God! Our God is an awe-some God!

TEXT: Rich Mullins
MUSIC: Rich Mullins

166   # Give Thanks

TEXT: Henry Smith
MUSIC: Henry Smith

rich," be-cause of what the Lord has done for us. And

us. Give thanks!

He Is Lord
167

He is Lord, He is Lord! He is ris-en from the dead and He is Lord!

Ev-ery knee shall bow, ev-ery tongue con-fess that Je - sus Christ is Lord.

TEXT: Based on Philippians 2:10-11
MUSIC: Traditional;arranged by Tom Fettke

168   He Has Made Me Glad (I Will Enter His Gates)

I will en-ter His gates with thanks-giv-ing in my heart; I will en-ter His courts with praise. I will say, "This is the day that the Lord has made!" I will re-joice for He has made me glad. He has made me glad, He has made me glad, I will re-joice for He has made me glad. will re-joice for He has made me glad.

TEXT: Leona Von Brethorst
MUSIC: Leona Von Brethorst

Find Us Faithful

O may all who come be-hind us find us faith - ful;

May the fire of our de-vo - tion light their way.

May the foot-prints that we leave Lead them to be - lieve,

And the lives we live in - spire them to o - bey.

O may all who come be-hind us find us faith - ful.

170 Shine, Jesus, Shine

1. Lord, the light of Your love is shin - ing, In the midst of the
2. Lord, I come to Your awe - some pres - ence, From the shad - ows in -
3. As we gaze on Your king - ly bright - ness So our fac - es dis -

dark - ness shin - ing; Je - sus, Light of the world, shine up - on us,
to Your ra - diance; By the blood I may en - ter Your bright - ness;
play Your like - ness, Ev - er chang - ing from glo - ry to glo - ry;

Set us free by the truth You now bring us; Shine on me,
Search me, try me, con - sume all my dark - ness; Shine on me,
Mir - rored here, may our lives tell Your sto - ry; Shine on me,

Shine on me. Shine, Je - sus, shine, fill this
Shine on me. Flow, riv - er, flow, flood the
Shine on me.

TEXT: Graham Kendrick
MUSIC: Graham Kendrick

land with the Fa-ther's glo-ry. Blaze, Spir-it, blaze; set our
na - tions with grace and mer-cy. Send forth Your Word, Lord, and

1 hearts on fire.

2 let there be light.

I Love You, Lord 171

I love You, O Lord, my strength. Psalm 18:1

I love You, Lord, and I lift my voice To wor-ship
You, O my soul, re-joice! Take joy, my King, in
what You hear: May it be a sweet, sweet sound in Your ear.

TEXT: Laurie Klein
MUSIC: Laurie Klein
© 1978 HOUSE OF MERCY MUSIC

172 My Life Is in You, Lord

My life is in You, Lord; My strength is in You, Lord; My

hope is in You, Lord; in You, it's in You. My life is in

2nd time to Coda

You, Lord; My strength is in You, Lord; My hope is in You, Lord; in

You, it's in You. I will praise You with all of my life,

I will praise You with all of my strength; With

TEXT: Daniel Gardner
MUSIC: Daniel Gardner

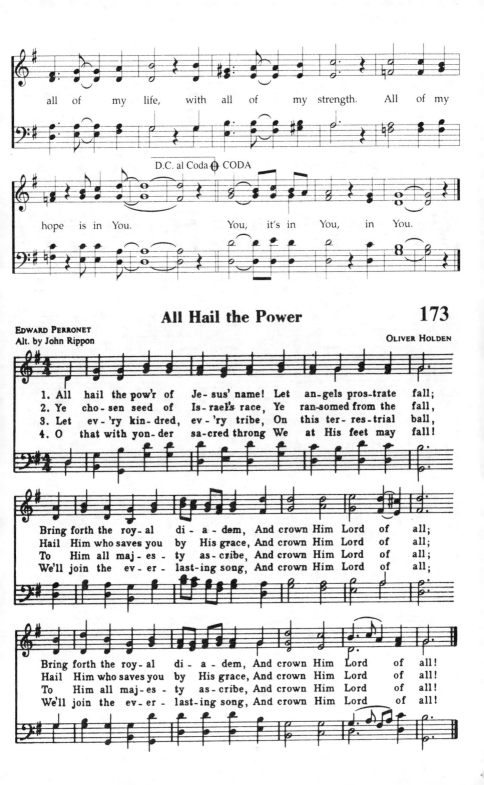

all of my life, with all of my strength. All of my

D.C. al Coda ⊕ CODA

hope is in You. You, it's in You, in You.

All Hail the Power 173

EDWARD PERRONET
Alt. by John Rippon

OLIVER HOLDEN

1. All hail the pow'r of Je-sus' name! Let an-gels pros-trate fall;
2. Ye cho-sen seed of Is-rael's race, Ye ran-somed from the fall,
3. Let ev-'ry kin-dred, ev-'ry tribe, On this ter-res-trial ball,
4. O that with yon-der sa-cred throng We at His feet may fall!

Bring forth the roy-al di-a-dem, And crown Him Lord of all;
Hail Him who saves you by His grace, And crown Him Lord of all;
To Him all maj-es-ty as-cribe, And crown Him Lord of all;
We'll join the ev-er-last-ing song, And crown Him Lord of all;

Bring forth the roy-al di-a-dem, And crown Him Lord of all!
Hail Him who saves you by His grace, And crown Him Lord of all!
To Him all maj-es-ty as-cribe, And crown Him Lord of all!
We'll join the ev-er-last-ing song, And crown Him Lord of all!

174 As the Deer

1. As the deer pant-eth for the wa-ter, So my soul long-eth af - ter Thee.
2. You're my friend and You are my broth-er, E-ven though You are a King.
3. I want You more than gold or sil-ver, On-ly You can sat - is - fy.

You a - lone are my heart's de-sire, And I long to wor - ship Thee.
I love You more than an - y oth-er, So much more than an - y - thing.
You a - lone are the real joy giv-er, And the ap - ple of my eye.

Refrain

You a - lone are my strength, my shield; To You a - lone may my spir - it yield. You a - lone are my heart's de - sire, And I long to wor - ship Thee.

TEXT: Martin Nystrom
MUSIC: Martin Nystrom

You Are My All in All

175

Part I *Unison*

1. You are my strength when I am weak, You are the trea-sure that I
2. Tak-ing my sin, my cross, my shame, Ris-ing a-gain I bless Your

seek; You are my all in all. Seek-ing You as a pre-cious
name; You are my all in all. When I fall down, You pick me

jewel, Lord, to give up, I'd be a fool; You are my all in all.
up; When I am dry, You fill my cup; You are my all in all.

Je - sus, Lamb of God, Wor-thy is Your name!

Je - sus, Lamb of God, Wor-thy is Your name!

TEXT: Dennis L. Jernigan
MUSIC: Dennis L. Jernigan

176   Change My Heart, O God

TEXT: Eddie Espinosa
MUSIC: Eddie Espinosa

177   **Are You Washed in the Blood?**

WORDS and MUSIC: Elisha A. Hoffman, 1878

Are they white as snow? Are you washed in the blood of the Lamb?

Come, Now Is the Time to Worship 178

Come, now is the time to wor - ship.

Come, now is the time to give your heart.

Come, just as your are, to

Words and Music by Brian Doerkson
© 1998 VINEYARD SONGS (UK/EIRE) ADMIN. BY MERCY/VINEYARD
PUBLISHING IN NORTH AMERICA (ASCAP)

wor - ship.

Come, just as you are,___ be -

fore your___ God.

Come.

One day ev - 'ry tongue will con - fess___ You are God,___

one day ev - 'ry knee___ will bow.___

Still, the great-est treas-ure re-mains____ for those____ who glad-

-ly choose____ You now.____

179

Shout to the Lord

My Je - sus, my Sav - ior;

Lord, there is none like You. All of my days

I want to praise the won-ders of Your

might - y love.

My com - fort, my shel - ter,

Words and Music by Darlene Zschech

I'll Fly Away

TEXT: Albert E. Brumley
MUSIC: Albert E. Brumley

Until Then

181

1. My heart can sing when I pause to re-mem-ber
2. The things of earth will dim and lose their val-ue,
3. This wea-ry world with all its toil and strug-gle

A heart-ache
If we re-
May take its

here is but a step-ping stone
call, they're bor-rowed for a-while;
toll of mis-er-y and strife;

A - long a trail that's wind-ing
And things of earth that cause the
The soul of man is like a

al - ways up-ward—
heart to trem - ble,
wait - ing fal-con—

This trou-bled world is not my fi-nal home.
Re - mem-bered there, will on-ly bring a smile.
When it's re - leased, it's des-tined for the skies.

Refrain

But un - til then my heart will go on sing-ing, Un - til

then with joy I'll car-ry on— Un - til the day my

TEXT: Stuart Hamblen
MUSIC: Stuart Hamblen

eyes be-hold the cit - y, Un - til the day God calls me home.

Blest Be the Tie That Binds 182

JOHN FAWCETT

HANS G. NAEGELI

1. Blest be the tie that binds Our hearts in Chris- tian love! The
2. Be - fore our Fa - ther's throne We pour our ar - dent prayers; Our
3. We share our mu - tual woes, Our mu - tual bur - dens bear; And
4. When we a - sun - der part It gives us in - ward pain; But

fel - low-ship of kin - dred minds Is like to that a - bove.
fears, our hopes, our aims are one, Our com - forts and our cares.
oft - en for each oth - er flows The sym - pa - thiz - ing tear.
we shall still be joined in heart, And hope to meet a - gain.

The Gideon Circle

A meaningful tradition in the Gideons at the conclusion of Gideon camp meetings, rallies, and fellowship dinners is the formation of THE GIDEON CIRCLE with singing of two stanzas of the hymn, *Blest Be the Tie That Binds*, just before the closing prayer. This is an optional choice in concluding these types of meetings.

If used, the procedure is as follows: The group stands to form the circle, joining hands (indicating unity in the Spirit), and sings the first and last stanzas of *Blest Be the Tie That Binds*. During the singing of the next to the last line of the last stanza, "But we shall still be joined in heart," the joined hands are slowly raised to slightly above head-level and are then slowly lowered during the singing of the last line, "And hope to meet again." The raising of the hands in unity reminds us of our future home together in heaven. A prayer of benediction closes the meeting.

INDEX